W9-DGD-060

A GEOGRAPHY OF
geography

THE BROWN
FOUNDATIONS OF GEOGRAPHY
SERIES

Consulting Editor
ROBERT H. FUSON
University of South Florida

A Geography of the Atmosphere
John J. Hidore, Indiana University

A Geography of Earth Form
Stuart C. Rothwell, University of South Florida

A Geography of Geography
Robert H. Fuson, University of South Florida

A Geography of Minerals
Walter H. Voskuil, University of Nevada

THE BROWN
FOUNDATIONS OF GEOGRAPHY
SERIES

A GEOGRAPHY OF
geography

ORIGINS AND DEVELOPMENT OF THE DISCIPLINE

ROBERT H. FUSON
University of South Florida

WM. C. BROWN COMPANY PUBLISHERS
DUBUQUE, IOWA

THE BROWN
FOUNDATIONS OF GEOGRAPHY
SERIES

Consulting Editor
  ROBERT H. FUSON
  University of South Florida

Copyright © 1969 by
Wm. C. Brown Company Publishers

Library of Congress Catalog Card Number: 73-84085

ISBN 0−697−05155−2

Second Printing, 1970

Printed in the United States of America

Geography is one of man's oldest sciences, yet it is as new as the Space Age. Knowledge of the earth obtained from satellite photography and measurement, remote sensing of the environment, and by means of other sophisticated techniques are really but a stage in the evolutionary process that began with ancient man's curiosity about his surroundings. Man has always been interested in the earth and the things on it. Today this interest may be channeled through the discipline of geography, which offers one means of organizing a vast amount of physical and cultural information.

The **Brown Foundations of Geography Series** has been created to facilitate the study of physical, cultural, and methodological geography at the college level. The **Series** is a carefully selected group of titles that covers the wide spectrum of basic geography. While the individual titles are self-contained, collectively they comprise a modern synthesis of major geographical principles. The underlying theme of each book is to foster an awareness of geography as an imaginative, evolving science.

To Fred Bowerman Kniffen

a geographer's geographer

Preface

The story of geography is one of a long journey through time and space. The route is many thousands of miles in length, traversing rain forests and deserts, mountains and plains, tundra and oceans. All told it has taken about 10,000 years for geography to get where it is today.

The sojourn has been one of high adventure; to find geography in the making one merely must find where the action is (or was) taking place. Our founding fathers include philosopher kings and despots, pirates and merchants, legendary super heros and quite a few real ones, priests and pagans, sailors and sheiks, poets and professors, explorers and cartographers. Some sailed with the Phoenicians and Vikings; others (such as Colonel Frank Borman, Captain James Lovell, Jr., and Lt. Col. William Anders, in *Apollo* 8) have orbited the moon in spacecraft. Such is the flavor of geography's origins and development.

The idea to write a brief account of the development of geography first occurred to the author fifteen years ago when he was a student of Dr. Fred B. Kniffen at Louisiana State University. It is hoped that some of that great geographer's inspiration is retained in the pages that follow.

The geography staff at the University of South Florida has offered many suggestions along the way. Hundreds of students have made anonymous contributions. My wife, Amelia, has been a patient and understanding critic. And most especially, grateful appreciation is extended to Mrs. Phyllis Patterson who typed the final manuscript and made many invaluable suggestions.

Contents

Chapter 1

The Oriental Origins

Near East and Beyond

Geography, both theoretical and practical, has a long and well-documented history. Since about the sixth century B.C., when the Aegean world began to produce a profusion of early geographers, the record is reasonably detailed. But before that time there existed a fund of both ideas and knowledge among the peoples of Mycenae, Crete, and lands to the east. Discovering just what this knowledge was, and who those ancient contributors were, is the task before us.

There is every reason to believe that very little theoretical geography existed before the Aegean period. Geographic thought, like other human ideas, cannot be recovered directly from archaeological excavations. To a large degree this is how we have obtained most of our information concerning the very early cultures. It is possible to recover fragments of the material culture, but attempts to reconstruct the thought processes that lay behind these artifacts are always open to question. Not until man began to write, work accurately with numbers, and draw reasonable maps did he leave a clear picture of what he was thinking as well as doing. Pre-Aegean man probably did think geographically on occasion; he behaved geographically on many occasions.[1]

In order to discover the likely sources of early geographic activity it is necessary to make a few assumptions. The first is that ideas and knowledge flowed to the Aegean from the east, and to a lesser extent from the south (Egypt). A second assumption is that Mycenaean contributions to Aegean geography were virtually nil. A third assumption is

---

[1]To "think geographically" is to understand certain fundamental man-land or spatial relationships. One may think geographically without being a geographer, as one may behave geographically without formal training. Geography is, to the author, that science concerned with *place*. It considers the physical and human interrelationships within a given place and the interrelationships between and among places.

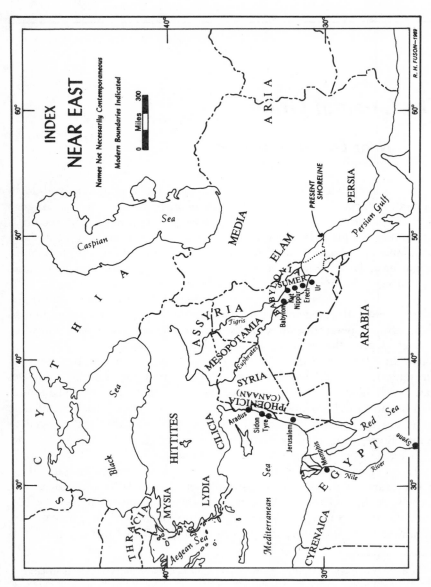

FIGURE 1.1. Index Map of Near East

that many of the attributes of high civilization, possessed by the peoples of the Near East, had their origins as far away as Southeast Asia. A fourth assumption is that little comes to geography from Paleolithic or Mesolithic man. Although hunters and gatherers did make trial-and-error discoveries about nature and their relation to it their behavior was more ecological than geographical. A fifth assumption is that the history of geography does not really begin to unfold until man entered the Neolithic Age. With the discovery of plant and animal domestication (not always in that order or at the same time) man found himself on the threshold of also discovering geography as we understand it today.

The discovery of farming (ca. 8000 B.C.) was the first great "revolution" this planet was to witness. We cannot be certain where this happened or who it happened to, but Southeast Asia is perhaps the best choice of locale. We are fairly sure that the great Desert River civilizations borrowed not only the idea of plant cultivation from peoples to the east, but many of the plants themselves and, perhaps even more important, the idea of irrigation. As intriguing as this subject is, however, the where, who, and why of agricultural origins is not germane to the present discussion. What is significant are the changes wrought by its discovery.

Radical modifications to human existence followed the advent of farming. Population increased, settlements became not only larger but more permanent, and society evolved into something much more complex than it had been in the days before farming. But of all the by-products of agriculture, two seem to stand out as they relate to our history. (1) *Leisure time* was created for at least some of the population, and (2) *planning* became almost a necessity.

The first of these by-products of the agricultural revolution, the creation of leisure, made it possible for the first time in human history to release relatively large numbers of people from the on-going task of food production. Though some of the more successful non-farming societies were able to do this in scattered instances, there really can be no comparison in numbers of people involved or in area affected. There was now time for a type of primitive professionalism. There emerged full-time priests, potters, weavers, metalsmiths, builders, and a variety of other craftsmen, including even politicians. Simply put, society had reached a point where it could no longer conduct its affairs on a day-to-day basis.

Geographic-like thinking probably began in conjunction with planning. There was an early need to understand the march of seasons, soil, water control, and related matters. Land distribution and acquisition were also urgent considerations. Defense from nomadic marauders and

protection of land from neighboring farmers required solutions. Among
the developments spawned by these and other problems of direct importance to geography's history would be the production of the first
good calendars, innovations in weighing and measuring, and local
mapping. For some peoples there also came a knowledge of distant
lands and nations as trade routes were opened. While none of these
occurrences could be called geography, they were indispensable blocks
in the foundation.

Another fundamental requisite for a culture that contributed to the
growth of our discipline may be defined as the *dynamic quality*. For
whatever the reason, no significant items were added to the geographic
inventory by static societies. *Movement* seems to be important to the
growth of geography. It may manifest itself in many ways: land acquisition, long-distance trade by land or water, exploration, colonization,
conquest, and on rare occasions, by sheer intellectual fervor. It is interesting to pose a question at this point: What influence does the geographic
environment have on the development of geographic thought, inasmuch
as there may be some connection between movement and the physical
environment? Surely an area situated in the path of movement would be
favored and would possibly produce the synthesis prompted by the
diverse elements flowing to and through it. In such a case the movement
of others (or their ideas) might afford a stationary culture the opportunity to be creative, and it might spur them on to additional movement
in their own right. With this in mind, let us review a few of the dynamic
societies of the Near East.

The Sumerians

Sometime between 5000 and 4000 B.C. there settled in the Tigris-
Euphrates delta region a people known as the Sumerians. Virtually nothing is certain as to their origin, though it may have been northwestward.
From this Semitic group spring all subsequent cultures in Mesopotamia.
If the Sumerians did nothing else they taught the world to write. The
earliest example of true writing comes from the Sumerian temple of
Inanna (at Erech, now Warka) and is dated ca. 3500 B.C. Geographers
should be pleased to note that the clay tablets of Inanna deal with many
aspects of the natural environment, especially plants and animals.

By the time the cuneiform tablets were inscribed the entire area
had already been subdivided into city-states. Also by this time these
city-states were already fighting frequent wars with each other over
land and water rights. Though they may not have produced any profound geographical theories in the fourth millennium B.C., the Sumerians
were clearly engaged in man-land relationships! It is quite possible
(even probable) that Sumerian concern for water rights and land owner-

ship resulted in the first maps. By 2250 B.C. the Sumerians had produced a "world" map to depict the military excursions of their great King Sargon (Fig. 1.2). Sargon not only conquered the independent city-states of Mesopotamia but established the first empire in history. The pattern he established was emulated by later rulers of Ur and Babylon, and by the Hittites and the Egyptians.

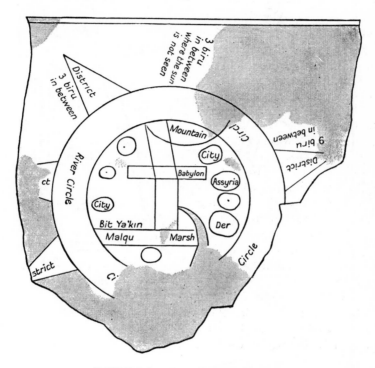

FIGURE 1.2. Sumerian World Map

From: Dickinson & Howarth, *The Making of Geography*, Oxford: The Clarendon Press, 1933. (Used by permission)

Sumerian conquests extended into Turkey and seem to have been prompted by a quest for raw materials, especially metals for armaments. It is interesting to speculate whether or not attempts to expand agricultural production in the delta area of Mesopotamia led to warfare, which in turn provided the impetus to seek new sources of metals. In any event, we have here an example of how an agricultural people become expansionists despite the fact that farming is usually thought to be a settling force on a society.

The Sumerians, by virtue of their forays into other lands, gained some of the perspective necessary for true geographic thought. The fact that they attempted to map the world as they understood it to be is evidence of this. As might be expected, most societies build up a vast amount of knowledge about their local area before tackling the entire globe. The Sumerians must have done this also, for maps of fields and canals were especially well-developed (Fig. 1.3). In addition to maps,

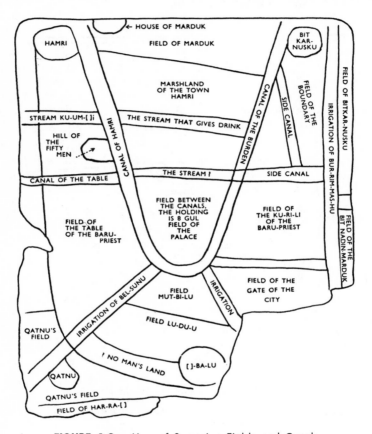

FIGURE 1.3. Map of Sumerian Fields and Canals

Courtesy of the University Museum, University of Pennsylvania, Philadelphia, Pa.

laws pertaining to land-use and water-use were extensive. Though not the first, the Code of Hammurabi (ca. 1760 B.C.) affords an excellent illustration.

The widespread canalization practiced in Mesopotamia at a very early date required intensive geographic knowledge, especially as it related to topography and soil. Though the canal system was an engineering marvel, there is no reason why it should be viewed as engineering alone. Such projects were classic examples of applied geography, requiring the collection of a massive amount of local geographic data. The greatest canal of the ancient world (and one of the largest ever constructed at any time) was the Nahrwan Canal. It was over 400 feet wide and extended for something more than 200 miles. Very little is known of this vast undertaking, but it irrigated the area east of the Tigris River, north of Kut.

Planning in early Mesopotamian culture involved more than fields and water control. A great deal of energy went into the development of royal parks, and plants of all sorts were imported from great distances. The most famous of these parks (though not the largest) was the Hanging Gardens of the Palace of King Nebuchadrezzar at Babylon, considered to be one of the Seven Wonders of the Ancient World. From the time of Sargon I to Herodotus (fifth century B.C.) every foreign conquest by a Mesopotamian ruler resulted in the importation of exotic plants. Rather exact written records were kept, and from them we learn production statistics, experiments conducted, and the types of plants cultivated. These records tell us, for instance, of the first time cotton was grown in the area (during the latter part of the eighth century B.C.). It is from a Persian word for this type of enclosed park that we inherit the word "paradise."

The Babylonians

Pure and plentiful water nourished the towns of Mesopotamia, and on occasion it was used to destroy a few of them. Ancient Babylon suffered from such a fate. Though the great city might have been weakened by siltation, sedimentation, and weedy growth clogging the extensive canal system (caused largely by deforestation, overgrazing, and erosion upstream), it was virtually wiped from the surface of the earth by a man-made flood. In 689 B.C., Sennacherib of Assyria diverted canal water through Babylon and reduced the proud city to a marshland. For a number of years the site was inhabited only by jackals, and though eventually rebuilt, never returned to its past glory.

But what a glory it had for more than a thousand years prior to the Assyrian onslaught. During this time Babylon produced more than its share of geographical elements. A few were of such profound importance that they are still in use today with little modification; others were absolutely indispensable to the development of any later geographic thought.

Can one even conceive of science without the mathematical concept of *zero*? Ponder for a moment where geography would be. Mankind will forever be indebted to the Babylonians for this discovery. Over the whole span of human existence only two cultures have ever hit upon the idea of a written symbolic expression for nothing: the Babylonians and the Maya Indians of Meso-America.

By 1800 B.C. Babylonian mathematics were well developed. By this time (and probably much earlier) we have a culture that can handle algebraic and geometric problems with ease. We still follow the example set by the Babylonian sexagesimal system of numeration (based on the number 60) when we express 5°30' or 3:15 A.M. And our much-cherished decimal system is but a later alteration of the Babylonian sexagesimal system, where the second step (60) is replaced by ten.

It was this highly sophisticated system of mathematics that made it possible for the Babylonians to develop an equally intricate system of astronomy some years later. Unfortunately, much of the Mesopotamian record between 1500 B.C. and 300 B.C. has been lost, but 500 B.C. is not too early a date to assign to full-fledged Babylonian astronomy. It may date from 1000 B.C. Though it is beyond the scope of this discussion to probe deeply into another branch of knowledge, a few outstanding achievements require a mention.

Babylonian astronomy *begins* at about the place where Egyptian astronomy terminates, yet the two peoples were contemporaries. In fact, Mesopotamia was so far ahead of its neighbor in astronomy that Egypt would have to be classed as a second-rate scientific nation for that period. Babylon discovered the ecliptic, or the apparent orbit of the sun against the background of stars. It correctly correlated solar years and lunar months (19 solar years = 235 lunar months). Planetary retrogradation was fully understood, and the Babylonians could predict, with great accuracy, solar and lunar eclipses and the first visibility of the planets and moon. They also gave the world the first gnomon, a simple instrument that could indicate time as well as the sun's meridian altitude. It may have been the Babylonians who first discovered the sphericity of the earth.

The Phoenicians

Phoenician culture probably evolved in Mesopotamia before the Sumerian period and, for some reason which we will probably never ascertain, they migrated across the Fertile Crescent to the shores of what are now Lebanon and northern Israel. In ancient days the Mediterranean coastal homeland of the Phoenicians was called Canaan and the people Canaanites. Also, we find them being referred to as Sidonians by both Homer and the Old Testament. The Phoenicians chose to settle as close to the sea as possible—why would a formerly inland people do this?—and some of their settlements (such as Tyre, Sidon, Aradus, and

Carthage) were actually on islands before lagoon silting joined them to the mainland.

Little is known of the earliest Phoenician period, and we first hear of Phoenicia when it was conquered by Egypt ca. 1600 B.C. Some 400 years later Phoenicia managed to gain its independence from Egypt, but it was troubled by strong neighbors on many occasions, eventually fading into extinction under Roman rule during the second or third centuries A.D.

Phoenician contributions to geography are enigmatic. They certainly were not predisposed toward theoretical matters, and even practical aspects of their lives were veiled. The people of Phoenicia may have done significant work in chartmaking, but their secretive nature has forever denied to us the opportunity to find out. In order to protect their far-flung sources of wealth, the Phoenicians carefully guarded almost all of their knowledge of other lands. A storehouse of ancient wisdom concerning winds, currents, tides, weather, harbors, navigation, and remote regions is seemingly unrecoverable.

The people of Canaan founded colonies throughout the Mediterranean area and perhaps beyond. Among the more important settlements were those of Cyprus, Sicily, Malta, Sardinia, Corsica, northwest Africa (Tunisia, Algeria, and Morocco), Spain (southeast and northwest), and the Scilly Islands (off Land's End, England). They maintained trading posts on the Greek Aegean islands and on the Isthmus of Corinth. The tin mines of Cornwall (England) may have been worked by them. There is a remote possibility that Phoenician ships plied the waters of northern Europe to obtain amber from the Baltic region (though they probably received it from overland traders at the head of the Adriatic Sea).

Phoenician coins of the fourth century B.C. have been found in the Azores and a variety of Greek and Roman legends hint at voyages as far west as America. Such an undertaking would not have been too difficult for these superb sailors. The great Carthaginian Hanno sailed down the coast of western Africa (in ca. 600 B.C.) to just beyond modern Sierra Leone. He *may* have circumnavigated Africa a few years later, if we can believe this claim of Herodotus. Even if Hanno did not round Africa the Phoenicians were the master seamen and navigators of the ancient world. Every great power made use of Phoenician seapower at one time or another. Persia may have fought Greece, but at sea the Greeks encountered Phoenician ships in Persian employ. At a later date Alexander relied heavily on Canaanite craft, as did the kings of Assyria many years earlier.

But the Phoenicians did not confine their activities strictly to water: they served much of their world as middlemen. Essentially all of the external trade of Egypt and Babylon was under Phoenician tutelage. Their merchants were established in most of the leading cities of the Near East, southern Europe, and northern Africa. From Cádiz to Memphis, in Jerusalem and over to Babylon—the Phoenician trader was a common sight. Almost everything passing from the Near East (including Egypt) to Greece or further west passed through Phoenician hands. It may be presumed that at least a *few* geographical ideas diffused with trade goods such as incense, perfume, spices, amber, tin, gold, silver, iron, copper, textiles (especially those colored with Phoenicia's famous purple), and glassware. One can only wish that Phoenician knowledge had been made public, but secrecy was necessary to preserve their monopoly.

Once we part Phoenicia's shore there is nowhere to go but northwestward to the Aegean. Phoenicia's neighbors (excepting, of course, Babylon) contributed little. As mentioned beforehand, Egypt did little for our origins. Though the people along the Nile were obviously thoroughly familiar with their local geography, and practiced land measurement of a high order, they were well behind the Mesopotamians. And, in any event, what few ideas Egypt produced were channeled through the Phoenicians.

By the latter half of the seventh century B.C., the Aegeans had received sufficient outside help to be able to launch their own career. The foundations had been well laid, at least from the practical standpoint: writing, mathematics, astronomy, measurement, elementary mapping, navigation, engineering, and exploration. It was *theory* that remained in such short supply. None of the Eastern cultures really produced so much as a thimbleful. But, to pose a hypothetical question, could the Aegean Greeks have provided that theory and accomplished so much, so early, if there had been no Sumeria, Babylon, or Phoenicia? And what debt did the Mesopotamians owe to those unknown cultures that once lay eastward in the misty dawn of the Neolithic Age? These questions will never be fully answered, but the discovery of farming, which marked the first time that man began to think geographically, was perhaps the greatest gift of all.

The Ancient Hearth

World of the Aegeans

To this point almost nothing has been said about Greece. For one thing, the very name connotes a rather precise location, especially to students of modern geography. By far the largest number of Greek-speaking contributors to geographic thought did *not* live within the confines of the political territory that comprises the modern Greek state. In fact, if we exclude a few of the major philosophers (Plato and Aristotle) and kings (Alexander and Ptolemy I) not one single geographer of classical Greece was born in the state now called Greece. For some reason that is not easily explained, most Greek geographic thought was produced by "colonials."

Another vexing problem concerns the role played by early non-Greek peoples that lived in what is now Greece. The foremost group of this sort was the Minoan, who inhabited the island of Crete between 2000 B.C. and 1400 B.C. This 160-mile-long island effectively separates the Aegean and Mediterranean Seas, and Homer has left us a vivid description. It may well be Crete that gave rise to the legend of Atlantis, for near the end of the Minoan Golden Age tremendous earthquakes, followed by tidal waves, wrought havoc on the benign island and caused an era to end.

We do not know where the Minoans of Crete came from, or when. They seem to have been seafarers, who were basically peaceful, and who brought with them much of the rich technology of the Near East. Apparently, Crete was settled by this highly advanced culture a few centuries before Sargon I united the warring states of Sumeria, or ca. 2400 B.C. Culturally there are many similarities with the Egyptian Old Kingdom (Sixth Dynasty).

From discoveries at the colossal Minoan center at Knossos (by Sir Arthur Evans in 1900), it is known that the Cretans had a written language (the so-called Linear A) that was not Greek and not even Indo-European. Also from Knossos comes Linear B, the oldest European inscription ever recovered. It is apparently written in archaic Greek, a tongue that entered the mainland from the north ca. 1900 B.C. The carriers of this early Greek language were the Mycenaeans, who established themselves in the rich Peloponnesian plain of Argive, a site inhabited by pre-Greek peoples for the thousand years previously.

The Mycenaeans were, in effect, the first Greeks, and the culture they possessed is known as the Bronze Age. Unlike the Minoans, they were warlike and aggressive, and within 300 years the balance of power shifted from Minoan Crete to Mycenaean Greece (ca. 1600 B.C.). After their ascendency the Mycenaeans begin to colonize the Aegean islands, coastal Turkey, and even Cyprus. Their mainland position was strengthened and Mycenaean culture was spread throughout the circum-Aegean region.

But Bronze Age civilization was not to last. By the twelfth century B.C. the world of the eastern Mediterranean was in chaos and crumbling. Greek cities were sacked and burned, Egyptian dominance in the Near East collapsed, the Hittite Empire fell, and, almost as a last desperate attempt to open the closed Black Sea grain routes, Troy was destroyed by King Agamemnon of Mycenae. These were the times and the peoples preserved by epic poems that Homer was to set down 400 years later.

What caused a Dark Age to descend on the Aegean world? Some scholars believe that the discovery and widespread use of iron was the principal reason. Bronze, long the metal of Crete, Mycenae, Egypt, and the Near East, was never in great supply and was essentially controlled by the established rulers. Iron, easier to work and superior to bronze for weaponry, made it possible for marauding tribes to defeat the old city-states, and even empires. Bronze Age culture died, with only memories of it maintained by means of an oral tradition. And by the *Iliad* and the *Odyssey*.

If Bronze Age Greece contributed to geography we have no record of it. The period was so completely erased that even Homer's epic tales were treated as sheer fantasy until Heinrich Schliemann unearthed Troy in 1871. Had not Schliemann been a non-professional archaeologist who had been thrilled as a boy by the high adventure of Homer (and who accepted the accounts of Troy as real) we might still know little or nothing of this phase of Bronze Age civilization.

Homer was a product of the Aegean Dark Age, and must have lived during the ninth century B.C. He seems to have been an inhabitant of what is now Turkey and might have lived anywhere along the Aegean coast of Asia Minor. He may have come from Miletus, a few miles south of the modern Turkish city of Söke, for this was the foremost eastern Greek city before 500 B.C. Also, Bronze Age artifacts have been found in the vicinity which attest to an ancient habitation. Toward the close of the Bronze Age, when trade collapsed and many of the mainland city-states found themselves isolated, thousands of people migrated to other regions. Homer might have descended from one of these settlements.

Written geography, or perhaps geographic-like writing, *might* have its origin with Homer. There is a great amount of geographic knowledge contained in the *Iliad* and *Odyssey*. Essentially, the *Iliad* treats of the local (Aegean) geography; the *Odyssey* is concerned with the distant reaches. Homer was extremely conversant with Aegean towns and cities (much of the *Iliad* is devoted to such an enumeration), and with most of the islands in the area. The saga of Ulysses (*Odyssey*) serves as a vehicle for boundless descriptions of the sea. He showed familiarity with winds, directions, and lands such as Africa (Libya). Homer also knew something of navigation and makes mention of the Great Bear (which guided Ulysses), though he does not seem to be familiar with Polaris. References to rather obscure star groups suggest that stellar nomenclature was advanced in the ninth century B.C. Homer dramatically describes alien lands and, though veiled by centuries of oral transpositions and later alterations, many areas are discernible. Some scholars now think the voyage of Ulysses to have been real, as might have been an earlier one of Jason and his crew aboard the vessel "Argo." Possibly Jason's was the first *recorded* voyage of exploration in history; surely it was one of the earliest by Europeans. Since Homer takes for granted (in the *Odyssey*) that the Voyage of the Argonauts is known by everyone, it is possible that parts of these two epic voyages were but one.

Though the name *Asian* appears in the *Iliad,* it is apparently a local name. *Europe* occurs in the Homeric *Hymn to Apollo* (ca. 700 B.C.) as a reference to the Greek mainland. From this point on the term seems to be extended to include all lands beyond Peloponnesus. In Greek mythology *Europa* was the sister of Cadmus, whom Zeus kidnapped and, in the form of a bull, carried to Crete. Among the mythical children created by the union of Europa and Zeus was Minos, king of the Cretans (Minoans).

Bunbury, in his classic *A History of Ancient Geography,* considers Homer to be both the father of geography and history. Strabo, writing two millennia ago, expressed the same belief. This would seem reasonable, for the epic poems not only recount historical facts but also provide us with the earliest description of ancient lands. For those who, like Schliemann, accept Homer's tales as largely factual, there is a treasure-house of geographic knowledge to be salvaged. Homer is the single bridge between Mycenaean (Bronze Age) Greece and the Classical

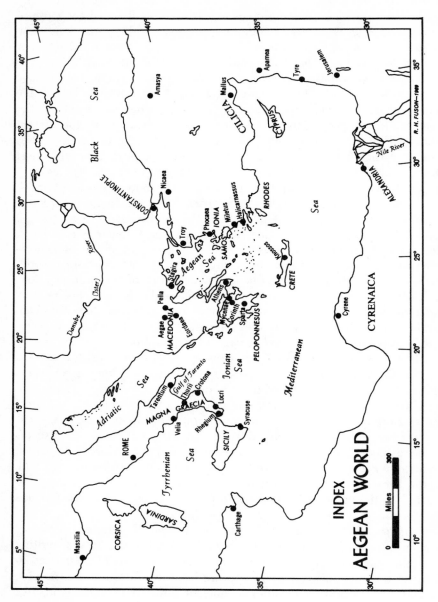

FIGURE 2.1. Index Map of the Aegean World

Greece that is to appear a century or two after his death. These epics of former greatness played no small role in providing the spark that was to be rekindled. It is through them that we are able to determine what sort of knowledge came to Greece's Golden Age from half a millennium earlier.

By the seventh century B.C. Homer had been dead for perhaps a hundred years, and the first Troy had lain in dust for 500 years. Sometime between the time of Troy and 700 B.C. many Greek colonies had been established. One of them was destined to produce more geographers than any city during the Golden Age.

Aegean Turkey (Miletus, Halicarnassus, Samos)

Miletus was located at the mouth of the Menderes (Maeander) River, in what was then Ionia and in what is now southwestern Turkey (37°30' N, 27°20' E). It may have been settled from Greece by 1200 B.C., and it was certainly well-established by 800 B.C. It was the greatest Greek city in Asia Minor before 500 B.C., and was responsible for the later establishment of more than 60 cities between the Dardanelles (Hellespont) and the Crimea. Miletus sponsored at least one trading center in Egypt (Naukratis). For centuries it thrived on trade and commerce flowing through its port, but by the sixth century A.D. the harbor had completely silted up and the site actually lies inland today. From Miletus came Thales, Anaximander, Anaximenes, and Hecataeus.

Thales (640-546 B.C.) was the founder of physical science and the Ionian school of philosophy. Considered to be one of the Seven Wise Men of ancient Greece, there are so many discoveries attributed to Thales that it is difficult to sort fact from fiction. His early fame seems to have been based upon his correct prediction of the solar eclipse of May 28, 585 B.C. But, inasmuch as Thales left no written statements, we must rely on accounts of later authors.

Thales introduced geometry to the Greeks and he is generally credited with five specific theorems. Tradition has it that he spent much time in Egypt and obtained his information there, but a Babylonian source is possible. Among some of the achievements attributed to Thales (but which were probably assigned to him long after his death by those who respected his wisdom) are the following: promoted the federation of Ionian cities, diverted a river, stated that moonlight was reflected sunlight, understood the ecliptic, studied the annual flooding of the Nile, taught navigators to steer by Ursa Minor rather than Ursa Major, by triangulation could measure heights and distances, and understood sufficient meteorology to predict a bumper olive crop and (by shrewd planning) was able to corner the market. Plato even tells of the time

Thales tumbled backwards into a well while studying the heavens, and suggested that this is what happens to someone who ignores what lies at his own feet.

Thales' notion of the cosmos makes one wonder if he really was as wise as his followers say. He viewed the earth as a disk floating on water. Water, it should be noted, was to Thales the fundamental element. As the basis for all life, water was treated in the same esteem by the Babylonians, Egyptians, and Thales.

Anaximander (611-547 B.C.) was Thales' principal disciple in Miletus. He is usually given the credit for introducing the gnomon (which he undoubtedly got from Mesopotamia) to the Greeks. Anaximander is also credited with one of the first world maps (which he constructed at least 2000 years after the Sumerian world map), based on waterfront yarns he picked up from sailors in Miletus. This map apparently was reproduced on bronze and, in ca. 499 B.C., the ruler of Miletus (Aristagoras) carried it all the way to Sparta when he went there to solicit aid in fighting the Persians. According to Herodotus, the map showed everything: rivers, seas, and *all* that surrounded these. In fact, the map was so well done that the Spartans, after seeing how far Persia was from their Peloponnesian homeland, rejected the whole idea.

Like Thales, Anaximander had some strange notions about the cosmos. The earth was shaped like a drum, with a circumference three times its height. Unlike most ancient theories, Anaximander's earth needed no support, for its center was equi-distant from everything. Without question, this was a highly sophisticated line of reasoning for the time. Several other ideas of Anaximander might be considered ahead of their time. He saw the earth's creation from a fiery mass that slowly solidified. Life, believed Anaximander, came from the sea (Thales' primary element, water). And he discussed the cycle of the seasons.

Anaximenes (ca. latter sixth century B.C.) followed Anaximander and, if remembered for nothing else, presented his disciples with a most extraordinary idea about the shape of the earth. He imagined our planet to be an irregular quadrangle (trapezium). Not only was it flat but it was held up by means of a most ingenious stuff: air pressure. This supporting air was a result of the earth's pressing down upon it, much like a piston compresses air in a cylinder. He never fully explained what held the air in position. Anaximenes did depart from tradition at one point. He said the sun and stars did not set and then circle beneath the earth to reappear on the other side. They supposedly circled above the earth at a great distance; on a regular schedule they passed behind high mountains and out of sight. He seems to have pointed to both refraction and condensation in his discussions. Concerning the latter he said, when air was "evenly distributed" it was invisible; upon condensing there was first mist, then clouds, then water, then solid matter. If the process were to continue there would be fire. High temperatures and aridity were caused by a scarcity of air; low temperatures and humidity, by density of air.

Hecataeus (ca. 550-ca. 475 B.C.), probably flourished between 520 and 500 B.C., and the dates of his birth and death are highly approximate. He occupies an extremely important place in the development of geography, for his written works represent an approach hitherto untried. Hecataeus produced the first books on historical and geographical topics written in standard prose. And these writings probably represent the first systematic description of the known world.

Hecataeus left two known works, though there may well have been others. The first, called *Genealogia* (or *Historiai*), deals with Greek folklore and traditions, but much of the book has been lost and only a few fragments survive. His second major work, *Ges periodos* (or *Periegesis; Tour Around the World*), is of more interest to students of geographic thought. This later work was in two parts: Part I is devoted to Europe, and Part II concerns Asia (and includes northern Africa). Hecataeus' map of the world (Fig. 2.2) was contained in *Tour Around the World*. This may have been a reproduction of Anaximander's world map, corrected and updated.

Hecataeus presents a rather orderly description of the known world in his geographical treatise. He begins with the area around his home base and works outward. His work is of great interest to ethnographers because of the careful attention he pays to obscure tribes of the Mediterranean region. Hecataeus does not venture beyond Gibraltar (the Pillars of Hercules) and seems to be totally unaware of the Atlantic and North Sea coasts of Europe. Even his description of the Black Sea area is disappointing, for there were numerous Greek colonies in the vicinity from which he could have drawn information. But, he demonstrates a remarkable awareness of India and mentions, for the first recorded time, the Indus River. Failure to discuss the Tigris-Euphrates region suggests he never travelled there; the detailed description of Egypt offers evidence that he had spent a great deal of time along the Nile.

For a long time (even in antiquity) the authenticity of Hecataeus' work was doubted. Today, however, classical scholars generally agree that the books were his and that later geographers (especially Herodotus) owe Hecataeus a great debt.

The Carian town of Halicarnassus (Bodrum in modern Turkey) lies just south of Miletus at 37° N, 27°32′ E. Despite the fact that it was just beyond the limits of Ionia, it was thoroughly Ionian in culture. Halicarnassus, though never a large town, had a fascinating history and produced its share of famous citizens. One of them was Dionysius (whose rhetoric won him fame in Rome during the time of Augustus). Another was Mausolus, who ruled about 370 B.C. His colossal tomb, built by Mausolus' widow and sister (in 353 B.C.), is known to us as the *Mausoleum* and was one of the Seven Wonders of the Ancient World. The little port also attracted the greats of history. It fought both Xerxes and

FIGURE 2.2. Hecataeus' Map of World

Used with the kind permission of John Murray, Publishers Ltd., London.

Alexander the Great (separately, of course) and lost each time. It was ruled by almost every major power in the region down through history: Persia, Egypt, and Rome, to mention three.

But, to geographers, Halicarnassus is most renown because it was the birthplace of Herodotus (484-425 B.C.). To many he is both the father of geography and history; to others (including this author) he was the culmination of an evolving geographic thought that had begun two centuries before with Thales. But, because Herodotus travelled extensively, because he wrote copiously, and because his writings have come down to us almost in totality, his place in our history is a very special one indeed.

Herodotus' monumental work (the *History*) is a history of the Greco-Persian wars. His detailed examination of the events and personalities connected with a conflict that lasted for more than a hundred years (ca. 546-448 B.C.) also served as a springboard for lengthy geographic digressions. There is even a possibility that he wrote the historical narrative first and then felt compelled to explain more about the peoples and places involved. There is the additional possibility that he never finished the *History*, for his narration ends with a battle that occurred in 479 B.C. (31 years before hostilities ceased).

The geography of Herodotus' *History* is the most detailed to be written up to this point in time. Unfortunately, it is not consistent. Quite clearly he omits vast quantities of material that were known to him. He quotes people (such as the Carthaginians) to back up his claims, then makes no mention of the people to whom he turned for support. Herodotus also found himself committed to certain philosophical notions about the earth that forced him to alter or even reject information that seems obvious to us now. With no shadow of proof he concluded that the Nile flowed in a west-east direction before turning to enter the Mediterranean. The idea of symmetry (so common to the Greek mind of old) compelled Herodotus to balance the Nile with the Danube (Ister), which he knew to flow in this general direction. And it also forced him to alter the direction of flow of the Danube's lower course (when he knew better) to make it conform to the characteristic sea entry of the Nile.

Herodotus made many gross errors on familiar ground (or sea), and was too cautious to really create. He rejected the idea of north European peoples (in the British Isles) though he was fully aware of the Phoenician tin trade in that area. He even denied the existence of the sea sailed upon by the Phoenicians to reach north Europe. But when describing areas he knew first-hand, this ancient geographer-historian had no peer in his day.

Herodotus was intimately acquainted with the Aegean region, and the entire coastal area of the Black Sea. He sailed part way up the Danube (there was a Greek colony at its mouth) and talked with numerous traders that had been as far as the Iron Gates (Romania-Yugoslavia), where rapids limited navigation. He had also taken a voyage up the Don River for some distance, and thereby offers us a lengthy ethnography of the Scythian inhabitants of what is now the Ukraine. Herodotus visited Persia, the Tigris-Euphrates region, the Phoenician coast, and spent a number of years in Egypt (venturing as far south as Aswan). In 443 B.C. he migrated to Thurii (Sybaris), on the west side of the Gulf of Taranto (now modern Italy).

Sometime before the move to Thurii he had been in Athens (the first of our early geographers that ever saw that city!) and had met Sophocles. Most of Herodotus' travels probably occurred before he had gone to Italy; certainly one of his sojourns in Egypt seems to have been about 460 B.C.

The present *History* is in nine books (arranged long after Herodotus' death) and rivals the epics of Homer in magnitude. In many ways the works are similar. They are both monumental. They were both "firsts" of their kind. They both had a tremendous impact on later generations. Each, in its own way, is a manifestation of the Greek mind and spirit. Though Herodotus was more "scientific" than Homer, he also was more restricted than Homer by a personal credo.

Lastly, Herodotus gave the world a map, which pretty well sums up his concept of our planet. Though it leaves something to be desired, it was the best map in the history of the world at its time. Even as far advanced as Herodotus was, when compared with some of his predecessors, he still seemed to view the earth as a flat disk. And, with a slight backward step, Herodotus deleted the ocean from western and northern Europe.

Samos (37°50′ N, 26°35′ E) gave the world Pythagoras (582-ca. 500 B.C.), but sometime before 530 B.C. Pythagoras was driven from there by the tyrant Polycrates. He emigrated to Crotona (see below) and the active portion of his life was spent there.

Magna Graecia (Crotona, Tarentum, Velia)

Sometime around the year 750 B.C. a group of Greek-speaking colonists settled the southern part of what is now Italy. Most of the colonies were coastal, lying along the shores of the "toe" and "heel" of the peninsula. Various city-states of the eastern Greek region contributed to the colonization. It is possible that some trading posts operated during the Mycenaean period, for trade was conducted between Italy and Greece during that period.

Three of the settlements in Magna Graecia played a significant role in the early development of geography: Crotona (now *Crotone*), Tarentum (now *Taranto*), and Velia (or Elea, now *Castellamare della Bruca*).

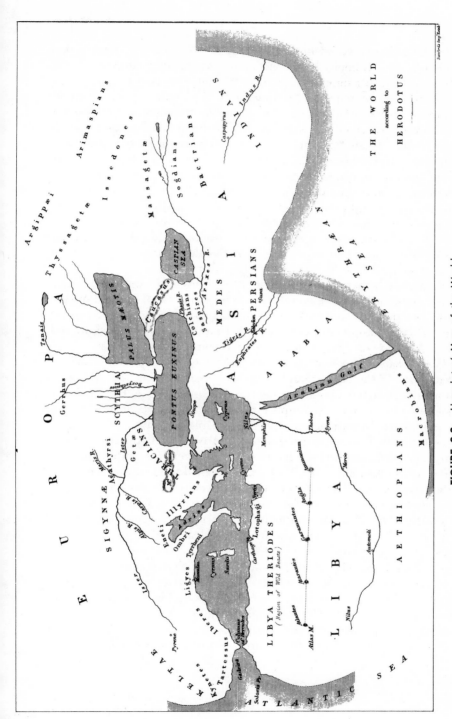

FIGURE 2.3. Herodotus' Map of the World

Used with the kind permission of John Murray, Publishers Ltd., London.

After Pythagoras settled in Crotona (39°05′ N, 17°05′ E) he became associated with a religious brotherhood that irrevocably altered his life. Eventually the brotherhood was to take his name.

The most startling notion to come from the Pythagoreans was the first concept of a spherical earth. Ionian geography (already discussed) still considered the inhabited earth to be flat for a century after Italian Greeks (*Italiotes*) had abandoned the idea. But, because the concept was so radically different from the traditional flat-earth one, it took many years for the fact to catch on. Some consider the discovery of a spherical earth to be *the single most fundamental principle of scientific geography*. Though many modern geographers continually pay homage to Herodotus as the "father" of geography, we could have survived without any of his ideas. Herodotus was mainly a reporter, not a creator. But without the global concept of the Pythagoreans there would be no geography at all.

The original spherical belief was a philosophical construct, based on an assumption that the sphere is the most perfect of all forms. Further, all the other planets, stars, and our sun and moon were believed to be spheres. These, along with a counterearth (*antichthon*), revolved around a central fire. So close is this to the Copernican theory that many years later Copernicus himself gave proper credit to the Pythagoreans for the discovery. It should be noted that, to Pythagoras and his disciples, the sun also revolved about the central fire. And the antichthon was invented to raise to ten the number of revolving objects in the system (sun, moon, earth, antichthon, five known planets, and fixed stars), because ten was held to be the perfect number. The Pythagoreans also held that the distances of the revolving bodies from the central fire and from each other was based upon a fixed numerical progression that could be determined. Accordingly, there is a relationship between Pythagorean studies of astronomy and music, for from the latter they learned the fixed relationship of a musical note to a length of string. From this ancient association we have inherited the idea of the "music of the spheres."

Often Philolaus (480- ? B.C.), a follower of Pythagoras, is credited with being the first man to conceive of a spherical earth. It is possible, but doubtful. Philolaus was a native of Tarentum, a town founded by the Spartans in ca. 700 B.C.[1] He is linked so closely with Pythagoras that it is difficult to always separate the two men. However, it is unlikely that one of the most basic Pythagorean tenets was formulated by a disciple.

---

[1]Some scholars say that Philolaus was born in Crotona, across the Gulf of Tarentum (Taranto). Crotona was settled by Achaeans ca. 710 B.C.

A development that could have come after Pythagoras is the scheme of dividing the earth into climatic zones. The Pythagoreans took the already existing divisions of the sky and transferred the idea to earth. On either side of the Equator they placed a central (equatorial) zone, then a winter/summer zone (considered to be the only one habitable), and the polar zone. The transfer of celestial divisions to the earth leads to the conclusion that the earth is the center of the universe, a notion held by later Pythagoreans and the forerunner of the Copernican theory. Inasmuch as the earth was *not* thought to be central by Pythagoras, it is logical to assume that someone else devised the tri-zonal system. Probably it was Parmenides (ca 519- ? B.C.), a native of Velia (40° N, 15°10′ E). Velia (or Elea) was founded in ca. 540 B.C. by Ionians. Here Parmenides founded the Eleatic school of philosophy, which also held that the earth was a sphere. It is probable that the Eleatic brotherhood was the first to place earth in the center of things; with this the later Pythagoreans came to agree.

In three small Greek colonies, during the sixth and fifth centuries B.C., there occurred a significant breakthrough in geographic thinking. At long last the retarding tradition of a flat earth was broken. It is not positive that the idea was indigenous with the scholars of Magna Graecia. It may have come from the Near East. Of the three men, only Pythagoras seems to have travelled widely. Though he was in Egypt his astronomical views are totally different from those on the Nile. It seems, then, that he did not learn much from the Egyptians. There is always the possibility of a Babylonian diffusion (via the Phoenicians?), for the sphericity of the earth was possibly first conceived in Mesopotamia. It really makes little difference at this juncture to debate the origin of the concept, for there is simply no proof on any side. And it is not critical whether the notion of sphericity came from philosophical or mathematical/astronomical endeavors. The idea did appear, and with it the promise of true geography.

Mainland Greece (Athens, Stagira, Pella, Eordaea)

One of the great historical paradoxes is: Why did the Greek mind contribute so many fundamental geographic concepts, and why were so few of these thinkers from the Greek mainland? Of the leading characters in our Greek cast, only *four* are from Greece proper, and none of these is usually thought of as a geographer.

One could, at this point, launch into a most interesting examination of the reasons underlying the *Greek Paradox*. Does living away from the homeland make one geographically more perceptive? Is the colonial culture somewhat different from the mother country, or is the physical setting the culprit? Did the city-state rivalry of Classical Greece aid the Greeks in their search for fresh ideas (as Dickinson and Howarth suggest), or did constant warfare on the mainland retard the progression of geographic thought?

Ponder the almost violent tone of Plato (427-347 B.C.) when he said that *the sea was responsible* for making men disloyal and unfaithful to neighboring city-states. Plato (the only native of Athens to earn a place in this brief analysis) may have become the first environmentalist when he wrote those words. Disillusioned with the strife ever-present (especially the Second Peloponnesian Wars of 431-404 B.C., and the Corinthian War of 394-387 B.C.) he sought explanations for such human behavior. The Greek World, unified by history, traditions, language, spirit, and an infinite array of culture traits, but hopelessly torn asunder by mountains and water—Plato saw these things underlying the success and failures of his people. The sea could be a unifying force, but distance of time and place often loosens this bond. Plato was especially aware of this latter condition. The cities of Magna Graecia, for instance, generally avoided the Peloponnesian Wars. Locri was strongly anti-Athenian, and Rhegium chose to be neutral in 415 B.C. To be true, the Italian colonies had problems of their own fighting non-Greek adversaries, and even mainland Greece tried to rescue them on several occasions.

Plato also had other reasons for blaming the sea for the actions of men. In 431 B.C., Athens and its empire existed because of Athenian naval supremacy. It was this maritime force that could (and did) threaten the sea-borne food supply of Corinth (coming from Sicily). Not only did Corinth appeal to Sparta for help, but many of the outlying Athenian territories were becoming restive. Sparta declared war, and the classic pattern was set: the Aegean's greatest naval power versus its strongest land power. To shorten the story of a 27-year war, but to show additional cause for Plato's aquatic determinism, let it be noted that the Athenian attempt to reduce Syracuse (Sicily) and Carthage (Tunisia) was a total disaster. Further, after a brief Athenian recovery, another (and the last) naval disaster occurred in Ionia (Turkish Aegean coast). Sparta had been successful in winning Persian support. Persian ships, manned largely by Phoenicians, decimated the Athenian fleet and the war ended. With its end the Athenian era went into an eclipse. Perhaps Plato was an environmentalist; perhaps he had reason to be one.

Before taking leave of the great philosopher we should mention his work *Timaeus*. In it he revives the legend of *Atlantis*, but now it is located beyond the Pillars of Hercules. Such a positioning was only possible because of the expansion of geographic knowledge that had occurred between the times of Homer and Plato. The original *Atlantis* was probably Crete; some men are still looking for the one misplaced by Plato.

Aristotle (384-322 B.C.) became a student of Plato when he was 18 years old. He was born in Stagira (40°30′ N, 23°50′ E), in Macedonia, where his father was a physician to the Macedonian court. Two of his works, *Peri Ouranou* (*On the Heavens*) and *Meteorologika* are of especial interest to geographers. Aristotle never did develop a descriptive geography; most of his thoughts center on the systematic aspects of the discipline. Perhaps this is just as well, for the few brief descriptive passages that do occur in his works are so thoroughly confused and utterly nonsensical that he might have done more harm than good.

Aristotle accepted the sphericity of the earth in the best Pythagorean tradition, and, in the best Eleatic style, placed the earth in the center of the universe. He not only noted the circular shadow of the earth on the moon during lunar eclipses, but correctly placed the earth between the sun and the moon at such times. He noted that the stars changed positions as one changed latitude and, from this observation, assumed that the earth was exceedingly small when compared to the cosmos as a whole and at a very great distance from the stars. Accepting certain calculations from mathematicians, he stated that the earth had a circumference of 400,000 *stadia*, or approximately 46,000 miles. He also accepted the earlier idea of three zones on either side of the Equator, saying that only the middle was habitable (the *oecumene*), but implying that there was a corresponding zone south of the Equator that *could* (not *did*) support a population. *Meteorologika* treats of many things: rain, snow, hail, weather changes, currents (which he incorrectly associated with sea depths), and alluvial deposition.

His ideas concerning the Atlantic Ocean are worth mentioning. Aristotle believed the Atlantic to be a very shallow sea. If *Atlantis* existed the sea would necessarily have been shallow over a recently submerged island of gigantic proportions (larger than Asia and Africa combined, according to Plato). Also, there is a report of a Phoenician voyage into an area of sluggish sea, where winds failed, and where a great amount of seaweed impeded navigation (the Sargasso Sea?). Surely the Phoenicians would play up every negative aspect of the sea beyond Gibraltar in order to protect their investments. If Aristotle is typical of the informed men of his time, then the Phoenician strategy worked exceptionally well.

When Aristotle was 41 years old he became the tutor of a 13-year-old lad in his native Macedonia. To this young boy Aristotle passed on the tradition of Plato and himself, and instructed the youth on such matters as how to be a king. Such was the inspiration acquired by Alexander the Great.

Alexander (356-322 B.C.), born in Pella (40°48′ N, 22°30′ E), capital of Macedonia, was destined to alter the course of geography as well as history. His expeditions (begun when he was only 21 years of age) added a vast amount of knowledge to the limited world known to the Greeks before that time. Not only did he push armies into Europe, Africa, and Asia, but he established contact with people who were almost mythical creatures beforehand. He ranged into Central Asia and as far east as the borders of India. Alexander's fleet cruised the Red and Arabian Seas, and the Persian Gulf.

This Macedonian was no ordinary conqueror. He was a dedicated explorer, who maintained a large staff of experts just to record and describe the several expeditions. Furthermore, official "pacers" provided the first long-distance land measurements ever taken. It is said that plant geography was born with Alexander's sojourns. Many new species were described and several were carried back to Europe.[2]

Not only was much more territory added to the current inventory, but many misconceptions were corrected. One error appeared, for some unknown reason, when the Caspian Sea, *after* observation, was said to empty into the ocean. Aristotle had spoken of it as completely enclosed, as earlier tradition had taught, but after Alexander's passage along its southern shores that sea was incorrectly mapped until the time of Claudius Ptolemaeus.

Alexander founded many cities that still bear his name, and many more that are now lost. The greatest of these, however, is Alexandria, Egypt, founded in 332 B.C. At the time of Alexander's arrival there existed a town called Rhacotis, dating from about 1500 B.C. To it he added a suburb called Neapolis. Together the old town and the newer addition became known collectively as Alexandria. It acquired the trade of the now-destroyed Tyre and became one of the world's most important cities by 250 B.C. For hundreds of years only Rome was to rival Alexandria.

The fourth and last of the mainland Greeks to receive our attention is Ptolemy I (367-283 B.C.).[3] Though born in Eordaea, Macedonia (40°20′ N, 21°40′ E), he is best known to geographers after he became established in Alexandria. But before we consider the men of Alexandria, let us take a fleeting glance at that side of Ptolemy unfamiliar to most of us.

---

[2]After Alexander's death India was penetrated to the Ganges. Most of the reports of these expeditions came from Megasthenes, whose original work is largely lost but preserved in the writings of Strabo and Arrian. Coming to us are the first notices of such things as sugar cane, rhinoceroses, rice, cotton, silk, and cinnamon.

[3]Ptolemy I should never be confused with Claudius Ptolemaeus, who flourished in the second century A.D. and was known generally as "Ptolemy."

Ptolemy's father was a Macedonian nobleman, and he had all of the advantages that befell royalty in his time. He was 31 years old when Philip II, king of Macedonia, was assassinated. The murder, which took place at the old Macedonian capital of Aegae, occurred while Philip was attending the wedding of his daughter. This incident had a marked influence on geography.

Philip's son, Alexander, became king of Macedonia at the age of twenty-one, and Ptolemy, a close friend of the family, became one of the young king's most trusted generals. The Persian campaigns had actually begun at the time of Philip's assassination, and one of the finest armies ever assembled was awaiting Alexander in the field. Ptolemy was to play a leading role in the campaigns in India and Afghanistan, and the year before Alexander died he arranged the marriage of Ptolemy and a Persian princess. Alexander's sudden and premature death in 323 B.C. (after a short bout with a strange fever) left Ptolemy in a position to inherit a major portion of Macedonian power. Ptolemy was appointed governor of Egypt by Alexander's successor, and when the struggle for power began among the several Macedonian leaders during the confusion that followed the death of Alexander, Ptolemy was content to consolidate his hold on Egypt.

Ptolemy I was not a kindly old benefactor-king who puttered away in the archives of Alexandria. He firmed up his Egyptian position by intrigue and murder. He even moved the body of Alexander against the wishes of almost everyone. Once securely established in Alexandria, Ptolemy launched a series of military campaigns, though his successes were not as continuous as those of his former master. He took Cyrenaica (northeast Libya), Cyprus, and Palestine. He eventually lost Cyprus, recaptured it, then lost again. He was in and out of Palestine on four different occasions. Ptolemy even occupied large portions of mainland Greece (including Corinth), and sections of the Aegean coast of Turkey. He became a hero to the people of Rhodes for his help in driving off the attacking Demetrius (and the Rhodians gave him the surname *Soter*, which means "savior"). But because of the fluid state of alliances in those days, and the ever-changing balance of power, Ptolemy I Soter retreated to the security of Egypt to rule for many years. So strong was the dynasty that he founded that Egypt was to be governed by Ptolemies for 350 years.

Egypt (Alexandria)

In many ways Alexandria is the first precise geographic location that became a fountainhead of geographic thought. Its site was carefully chosen by Alexander the Great, and its selection by Ptolemy I to serve as his capital was based principally on its superb geographic situation for commanding trade in the region. But it is because of its famous library that all modern scholars speak of Alexandria with such reverence.

The library at Alexandria was the most famous in the classical world. It was planned and organized by Demetrius Phalereus, brought from Athens by Ptolemy for the job. The library became the first large collection of documents in history, probably exceeding 500,000 in number at its peak. Most of the earlier material was recopied, and carefully edited to standardize spelling and punctuation. Also, there was a standardization of scrolls and the division of many works into "books," in order to facilitate storage and use. The library became the virtual home of some of the classical world's greatest minds, and its contributions to geography have been countless. One of the greatest tragedies that ever occurred to scholarship took place during the latter part of the third century A.D., when the library was totally destroyed during a civil war.

Ptolemy I Soter's contribution to geography, then, was a library.

Eratosthenes (276-194 B.C.), who was to become the head of the Alexandrian Library, was born in Cyrene (now Shahat, 32°50′ N, 21°45′ E), in what is now Libya. Eratosthenes came to Alexandria at an early age and undertook his first studies there. Later he went to Athens for additional studies before returning to his adopted city upon the invitation of Ptolemy III to take up his duties at the library.

Eratosthenes wrote mainly on subjects of a geographical, astronomical, or mathematical flavor. But he also was a poet and made contributions to the early literature on ethics and the theater. His work titled *Geographica* established the basis for mathematical geography. To geographers he is best known for making the first reasonably accurate measurement of the earth's circumference, for providing the world with the best map ever produced up to its time, and for laying the foundation of a new branch of geography: *geodesy*. With regard to the latter, it must be mentioned that Eratosthenes was the first to suggest that the earth was not a *perfect* sphere.

Despite all the scientific resources at his disposal, Eratosthenes, in calculating the circumference of the earth, resorted to one of the most incredibly remarkable measuring devices ever used by man: the camel. He had learned that it took a camel caravan 50 days to cover the distance between Syene (now *Aswan*, at the First Cataract on the Nile) and Alexandria. He also accepted the fact that Syene was on the Tropic of Cancer (it is not; Syene is at 24°05′30″ N), and also on Alexandria's meridian (again, no; Syene lies 2°59′ E of the meridian). Assuming that a camel covered 100 *stadia* a day, Eratosthenes calculated that Syene lay 5000 *stadia* to the south (actually the distance is 4250 *stadia*). By means of a gnomon, he measured the sun's altitude at noon on the summer solstice, and reasoned that 7.2° separated Alexandria and Syene. If 7.2° = 5000 *stadia*, then 360° = 252,000 *stadia*.

At this point we run into a small problem. The exact length of the *stade* used by Eratosthenes is unknown. If he used the one common to Athens (185 meters in length), then his measurement was 16 per cent too large for the circumference. We must assume that he was in error by at least this amount, for there is no plausible explanation of why he would alter the common unit of measurement. His circumference would have been approximately 29,000 statute miles. Eratosthenes' main problem at the time (and now ours!) was that he accepted the distance of 5000 *stadia*, which resulted in a value of about 700 *stadia* for each of his degrees, when in reality there are only about 600 *stadia* in a degree.

The world map (Fig. 2.4) of Eratosthenes gives us an idea of the geographical knowledge available to him. Several of the earlier errors are carried forth (such as the Caspian's supposed outlet and the Danube's origin in the Pyrenees), but the general gain in knowledge since the time of Herodotus (Fig. 2.3) is clearly evident.

France (Massilia, now Marseilles)

Before we alter the chronological sequence too much, let us make brief note of Pytheas (? - ca. 285 B.C.), who was a contemporary of Ptolemy I and Alexander the Great. He is introduced at this point because Eratosthenes based some of his world map on information supplied by Pytheas, and it is largely for his travels to distant lands that he is remembered today. Regrettably, his major work, *On the Ocean*, is lost. Only a fragment of another unnamed manuscript survives, which seems to be devoted to a description of the Mediterranean coast.

Our knowledge of Pytheas' writings comes from quotations by authors who were familiar with them while they were extant. Largely they concern themselves with travels beyond Gibraltar, and might have more than a casual relationship to the nature of Massilia itself. This city was founded by Phoenicians, possibly by 700 B.C. To this was added a Greek colony (ca. 600 B.C.), composed of immigrants from the Asian Minor city of Phocaea (now *Foca*; 38°40' N, 26°55' E).[4] Additional colonists arrived around 542 B.C., after the Persians took Phocaea and the adjacent cities. Far removed from its Aegean homeland the Massilians became essentially self-sufficient. They continued the sailing traditions of both the first Phoenician and later Phocaean inhabitants. Much of the southern coast of France and Spain witnessed Massilian influence and

---

[4]Phoenicia and Phocaea are totally unrelated despite the similarity of names.

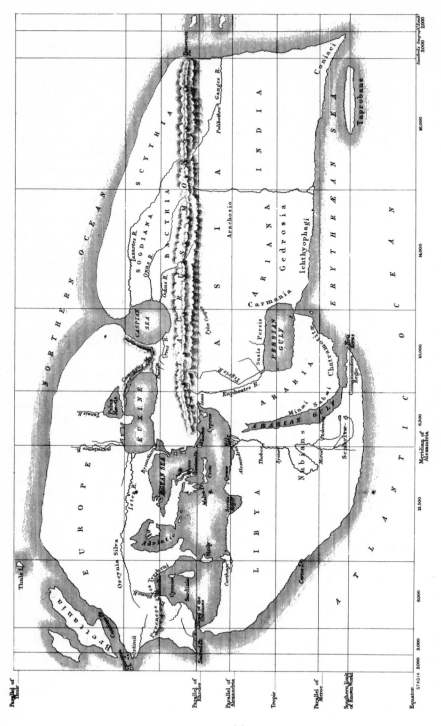

FIGURE 2.4. World Map of Eratosthenes

Used with the kind permission of John Murray, Publishers Ltd., London.

trading outposts. Inland trade was carried on, at least as far as the Alps, with wine being the principal commodity. Massilian navigators apparently ventured beyond the Pillars of Hercules on numerous occasions. The explorer Euthymenes sailed down the African coast to Cape Verde in the fourth century B.C. It was about this time when Pytheas sailed around the Iberian Peninsula to visit Britain, northern France, and the Low Countries. He may have gone as far as the Elbe River in Germany.

Pytheas was probably on a scouting expedition to seek some of the hidden sources of Phoenician wealth, derived largely from the tin and amber trade. He seems to have found amber, probably in the Schleswig-Holstein area, but it is doubtful that he reached the Baltic amber region. His reports of Britain neglect to mention the Scilly (Cassiterides or Tin) Islands which were being worked at that time by the Phoenicians. He does offer the first positive accounts of British and North European life, however, and proved to be a shrewd observer of cultural behavior.

Probably the best-known aspect of Pytheas' voyage is his report of a land called *Thule,* six days' sail north of Britain. He never said that he actually went there, though many writers assume he did. This land could be almost anywhere: Norway, the Shetlands, the Orkneys, Faeroe, or even Iceland. He did indicate that it was close to the Arctic Circle and, because Pytheas has proven to be an accurate astronomer, there is no reason to doubt him. In fact, his observations on the length of the daylight periods were used by later geographers (such as Eratosthenes) to establish parallels of latitude. He also noted the lunar influence on tides and observed that Polaris was not quite over the North Pole (it was even further removed than today and this observation would not have been difficult for a careful astronomer of that time).

Pytheas opened a new world with his account. Though rejected by many scholars in whole or in part (Strabo was a great doubter), much of his report has been verified. Fortunately for the development of geography, Eratosthenes did not reject the work.

Turkey (Mallus, Nicaea)

Our journey through space and time brings us back full circle, to Asia Minor. There in the town of Mallus (37° N, 35°20′ E), in the region of Cilicia, lived Crates (? - ca. 130 B.C.), a Stoic philosopher who is best known to everyone (but geographers!) for his commentaries on Homer. To geographers, however, he is the man who constructed the first known globe. And, because of philosophical requirements, to balance his globe he placed two land masses on the *unknown* side to bring the surface into harmony with land areas of the ancient world with which he was familiar.

A contemporary of Crates, Hipparchus, lived to the northwest in Nicaea (40°25' N, 27°50' E), about 25 miles south of the modern Turkish city of Izmit. Because of the Nicene Creed the site is well-known to Biblical scholars. Hipparchus (ca. 180-ca. 127 B.C.) not only worked at his birthplace, but also at Rhodes and the famous Library in Alexandria.

Hipparchus took it upon himself to improve on the map of Eratosthenes and bitterly criticized the work of the old master. His idea to construct a world map based upon accurate latitude and longitude measurements was commendable, but his final result was only a little bit better in places than the earlier one of Eratosthenes and a whole lot worse throughout. Despite his apparent dislike for Eratosthenes, Hipparchus happily accepted the previous determination of the earth's circumference. He made one contribution at this point (or rather, introduced a Babylonian idea into Greek thought): Hipparchus divided the great circle into 360°. He improved on Eratosthenes' principal parallel, which ran from Gibraltar through Rhodes, by correcting the position of Sicily. He further used the Alexandria meridian of Eratosthenes for his east-west determinations. Here we have another important refinement. Hipparchus drew eleven parallels of latitude, basing them on the length of the daylight period at each during the summer solstice. These *zones* of latitude he called *climata*, and it seems reasonably sure that this is the first use of this word in geography. We are not positive if he meant the parallels themselves or the regions bounded by the lines when he called them *climata*.

Hipparchus seems to have hit on the idea of determining longitude by the observation of solar eclipses, but inasmuch as he lacked the data he was unable to really establish meridians with any more accuracy than earlier astronomers. He also did not believe that the Western and Eastern Oceans were one. His observations of tidal differences strongly suggested that they were separated by an unknown land mass. This was truly a sophisticated idea for the time.

Syria (Apamea)

Poseidonius (ca. 135-50 B.C.) is the last geographer of the Aegean period we shall consider. By his time there was beginning to appear a decline in theoretical questions and geography becomes, as it seems to have begun, a more practical subject.

Apamea (35°20' N, 35°25' E), situated on the Orontes River of modern Syria, was founded in the fourth century B.C. It was an undistinguished city; perhaps that is why Poseidonius decided to try his luck at traveling. He visited the eastern Adriatic coast, Sicily, Italy, southern France, and Spain (where he spent many years at Cádiz). He was of the Stoic school and he did much to spread the philosophy throughout the Roman lands. Eventually he settled at Rhodes, where many great men came to study, including Cicero.

Poseidonius was the next man after Eratosthenes to attempt to determine the earth's circumference. His method was slightly different: he observed the star Canopus on the horizon of Rhodes at a time when he knew it was 7°30′ above the horizon at Alexandria. This established a central angle of 7°30′ (compared with 7°12′ for the central angle of Eratosthenes). His distance between Alexandria and Rhodes was determined by the time it took a ship to make the crossing (a measuring device no better than Eratosthenes' camel).

Actually his reading of Canopus was incorrect. The radius angle between Rhodes and Alexandria is 5°12′, not 7°30′. And the distance from Rhodes to Alexandria was miscalculated. To further complicate matters, Alexandria and Rhodes are not on the same meridian. Assuming, for the moment, that all of these errors are insignificant (which they are not), we are still not certain just what length *stade* Poseidonius used, If he used the Attic *stade* (185 meters), his circumference would have been about 27,000 miles. By correcting the distance between the two sites he would alter his circumference. Apparently he did this, and arrived at a circumference of 18,000 miles, if we are to believe later writers (such as Strabo) who consistently cite this figure. Either Poseidonius made a correction that is lost to us, or someone else made the correction, or someone else made an error. In any event, the figure of 18,000 for the circumference of the earth was not revised for 900 years, and the later figure (though nearly correct) never reached the eyes of Columbus and other fifteenth and early sixteenth century navigators and explorers. There is some reason to believe that Columbus might not have begun a voyage over an ocean of such dimensions had he possessed the correct calculations. Possibly this is an error that altered the course of world history and geographic exploration.

Chapter 3

On the Road

From Greece to Rome

Sometime during the second century B.C. Greek dominance in the field of geography began to falter. It is not an occurrence that can be precisely dated, for nothing of an evolutionary character has a sharp beginning. The rise of Rome as a power to be reckoned with must have triggered the Greek demise, and because Rome turned her attention first to the west, the Aegean world persisted beyond the entry of Rome into Mediterranean affairs.

Rome's immediate fear was Carthage, a state that controlled the western Mediterranean and had strong outposts in Sicily, Sardinia, and Corsica. The Greeks were also in Sicily (Syracuse), but their position was so insecure that they posed no threat to the peninsula. Events culminated in the First Punic War (265-241 B.C.) and Rome acquired Sicily and the small Lipari Islands (north of Sicily). In 239 B.C. Rome occupied Sardinia and Corsica, and by 222 B.C. the Celtic tribes in the north of the peninsula were subdued, thereby giving Rome control of the rich Po Valley.

But Carthage was not to remain inactive. Most of Mediterranean Spain was occupied by the Carthaginians before 219 B.C. The Carthaginian Hannibal was not to stop at the Ebro River; he crossed and attacked Saguntum, an independent seaport in Spain that had a defense pact with Rome. Further, Rome's ally, Massilia (Marseilles), was threatened with extinction by the advance of Hannibal, and Massilia placed its entire fleet under Roman command. The Second Punic War (218-211 B.C.) had begun. Despite a series of Carthaginian successes, Rome was able to muster its forces and again secure territories that had been conquered or had revolted. By 211 B.C. the mainland and Sicily were under Roman authority once again; by 206 B.C. Carthage was forced to leave Spain, and in 202 B.C. the Romans crossed to North Africa and defeated Carthage on its home territory.

From this time on, Rome had no opposition in the West. Now the Empire could turn its attention to the East, and by 189 B.C. the power of Rome extended throughout the eastern Mediterranean. But this was not the same sort of domination that was to be found in the West. In the West Rome ruled directly, and her customs, institutions, and language gradually replaced those of the lesser civilizations subdued. In the East, however, Rome entered to "liberate" the Greeks, and there was never the intensity of political domination. Largely because of this difference, the Greek mind survived, and even during Roman dominance, there remained scholars like Hipparchus (among many) that belonged to the Greek rather than the Roman school of geography.

There was, then, a time of overlap, during which Roman writers gradually replaced those of the Aegean tradition. During the first phases of the transition the tradition remained Greek, but the work was often produced in Rome, or after long years of residence in Rome.

Polybius (ca. 204-117 B.C.) was typical of writers during the transition. Though born in Megalopolis, Arcadia (in Peloponnesus), he was sent to Rome at the age of 37, where he remained for 17 years. He was a contemporary of Hipparchus, but was so intimately associated with the Romans that he seems more representative of that school.

Polybius was actually a hostage in Rome, taken as such after the Roman victory in the Second Macedonian War (167 B.C.). But he enjoyed relative freedom and participated in a number of important Roman expeditions. He was present at Carthage in 146 B.C., when Rome destroyed that city during the Third Punic War. Shortly after that time he returned to Greece and saw the recently destroyed Corinth. Polybius sailed along much of the North African coast, visited Alexandria, Rhodes, Sardis, and was witness to the Roman capture of Numantia (Spain), in 134 B.C. He also visited France, and followed the trail of Hannibal in crossing the Alps on the return to Italy. At one point he sailed through Gibraltar, down a portion of the Morocco coast.

Polybius was, in the main, an historian. He wrote a history of the period of 220-168 B.C., beginning with Hannibal in Spain and ending with the battle of Pydna (Macedonia). Of this work comprising 40 books, only a few are extant. One of them (the thirty-fourth) was a systematic geographical work. Polybius also wrote a treatise on equatorial regions.

Though an historian, Polybius never lost sight of the contribution geography makes to that subject. He weaves a geographic thread throughout all of his writings. Polybius is the first geo-historian to make full use of the new knowledge accrued from the Roman campaigns. From the widening arena he was able to make many significant contributions to measurements in the Mediterranean. And, while his own travels afforded a rich source of first-hand knowledge, he made wide use of written records from Rome, Rhodes, Alexandria, and Peloponnesus.

Perhaps the most significant contribution Polybius made to geography was to exert a strong influence on Strabo (64 B.C.-20 A.D.). Of all the geographic writers of antiquity, Strabo is best known today, because his *Geography* survives almost intact. Of 17 books, only a portion of the seventh is incomplete. It is possible that had Strabo's other major work (*History,* in 47 books) not been lost, he would have been revered for what he really was, an historian.

Strabo was born in Amasya (40°40′ N, 35°50′ E), in what is now Turkey. The city still exists, lying on the main road and railway between Samsun and Sivas. He was from a wealthy and influential family who provided him with a classical Greek education. When about 20 years old Strabo ventured to Rome to study under the geographer Tyrannion. Philosophically Strabo was a Stoic, believing (along with other Stoics) that things should conform with nature. He was quite obviously a great admirer of Rome and, in addition to his first visit, was in the city on at least three other occasions. He was in the Nile Valley (where he visited Syene in 24 B.C.) and lived for five years in Alexandria. He spent very little time in Greece proper, though he did pass through Corinth. It is possible that he was in Athens once, though most scholars think not. Strabo's later years seem to have been spent at his home in Amasya, where he died at the age of 84 years.

Strabo's *Geography* is perhaps as important for preserving certain lost works of writers like Eratosthenes, Polybius, and Poseidonius, as it is for conveying to us his own conceptions. It would be almost impossible to reconstruct much of early geography (as was done in Chapter 2) without this work. Actually, *Geography* must have been an appendix to his longer *History.* This latter work takes up from where Polybius stopped (after four introductory books) down to the death of Caesar. Later Strabo added the 17-book *Geography*: i-ii, the introduction; iii-x, Europe; xi-xvi, Asia; xvii, Africa.

Strabo's *Geography* is the first attempt to pull together all of the geographical knowledge available at that time. It is difficult to understand how he could have perpetuated so many errors, while at the same time bitterly attacking such writers as Herodotus, Pytheas, and Eratosthenes, who were often closer to the truth than Strabo. He called Pytheas an "arch-falsifier" about almost everything (especially his report of *Thule*); he wrote that Herodotus was a "compiler of fables" and totally untrustworthy; he took Eratosthenes to task for criticizing Homer and poetry in general. In fact, Strabo displayed a time-honored Greek trait when he almost deified Homer, whom he considered to be "the father of geography."

Strabo accepted the spheroidal character of the earth, and believed it to be divided into five zones. He argued that the geographer should describe the inhabited world (*oecumene*), and though Strabo stressed the importance of mathematical and physical aspects he demonstrated how inadequate his knowledge of these matters was. Strabo's belief that geography should be written to serve statesmen and the upper classes is a notion derived from Polybius. He said that geography was largely political; that it was of great importance to military undertakings.

Most of *Geography* was assembled from what we might call library research, though Strabo was apparently ignorant of many contemporary sources (a good argument that it was written in Amasya rather than in Rome). Certainly *Geography* attracted little (if any) attention during the first and second century A.D., which might be expected if it were compiled in Asia Minor. But by the sixth century it was established as one of the great works of all time, and was to set the pattern for a type of encyclopaedic geography that was to follow.

Strabo's world map (Fig. 3.1) offers a good summary of the knowledge he accepted. His idea of northwestern Europe was appalling, and he continued the error of giving the Caspian Sea an outlet. Though he improved on Eratosthenes' positioning of the Iberian peninsula, he rendered Italy in a most disturbing fashion for one who lived there. Strabo eliminated *Thule* and misplaced Ireland. Considering the fact that Eratosthenes worked 200 years earlier, it might be argued that despite Strabo's monumental descriptive geography, his *idea* of our planet was no further (if as far!) advanced.

The two decades following Strabo's death passed with no additions to the geographic literature. Even Strabo's work was to remain generally unknown for some time to come. However, in 43 A.D., the hiatus was ended with the publication of *De Situ Orbis* (or *De Chorographia*) by Pomponius Mela.

Almost nothing is known about Mela, yet he was the first geographer to write a purely geographical work in Latin. He flourished during the mid-first century A.D., and was born at Tingentera (now *Tarifa*), Spain's southernmost city on the Strait of Gibraltar.

Mela's little book was not in any way scientific or very original. Herodotus is the source for much of Mela's information, which means that Mela, at least in some instances, was 500 years out-of-date. He did not delve into mathematical geography one whit, and avoids any discussion of measurement. He repeats many of the old geographical fables concerning both people (with two heads, or goat feet) and places (the Danube emptied into the Adriatic Sea and Scandinavia was an island).

His earth was divided into five zones: torrid about the equatorial area, and a temperate and polar in each hemisphere. He noted that the

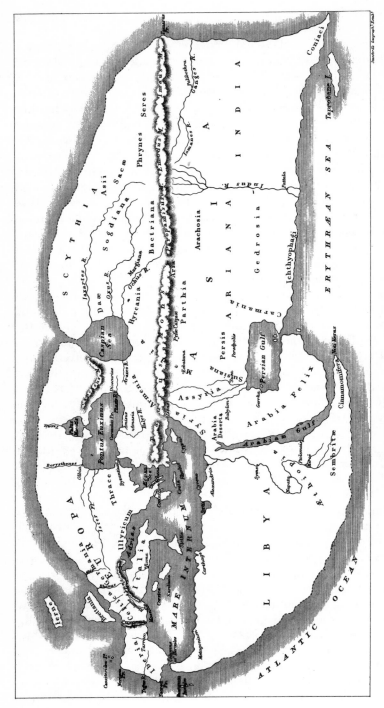

FIGURE 3.1. Strabo's Map of the World

Used with the kind permission of John Murray, Publishers Ltd., London.

southern temperate zone was inhabited by the *antichthones,* a people who could never be reached because of the unbearable heat of the torrid zone.

Mela's organization is unfortunate, for several areas are treated in entirely different portions of his little book. He first describes the three continents (Europe, Asia, and Africa), then, beginning with southern Spain, describes each country in order across North Africa to the Near East. From there he returns along the north side of the Mediterranean, taking each country in order. He next discusses all the islands of what he termed "Our Sea" (Mediterranean). Mela then followed the coast from southern Spain to the Baltic. He afterwards mentions the islands along the route, then returns to the east to describe the region between Arabia and India, and the coast of Africa. The net effect of all this was to place even his homeland (Spain) in two different locations within the text.

His knowledge of Spain and France was far superior to anything ever written earlier (including the great work of Strabo). In fact, his detailed description of parts of Spain and France show an intimate acquaintance. He also was better informed of Britain, and gave us the first account of the Orkney Islands. Mela returned Ireland (which he called Iuverna) to its proper position (Strabo had moved it too far northward), and restored Thule to the map.

Mela had access to certain knowledge that was made available as recently as the year he wrote, for in 43 A.D. Aulus Plautius landed four legions of Roman troops in Britain and commenced a serious conquest of the Islands. Though the Romans had been there a century before (under Caesar) their authority had never been applied with determination.

Several expeditions to follow were to broaden geographic horizons, but they occurred too late for Mela to incorporate into his work. There was a Roman penetration to the Baltic Sea, directly overland, and another up the Nile to at least 9° N. This last position was not again visited by a European until 1800 years later!

One contemporary of Mela should be noted, and it is of interest that he was another native of Spain. Lucius Annaeus Seneca (3 B.C.-65 A.D.) was born in Corduba (now *Córdoba*). We shall not dwell on the tragic life of the younger Seneca, which included a term of exile in Corsica and ended with an order by Emperor Nero to take his own life. It is ironic that Seneca was Nero's tutor when the latter was only 11 years old, and it was his influence over Nero that may have produced the hostility that resulted in Seneca's death.

Of his many writings, Seneca's *Naturales Quaestiones* (ca. 63 A.D.) is relevant to our story. It was a short (seven books), popular treatise on astronomy and meteorology. This work included a great deal of what might be termed physical geography and, because of Seneca's reputation in Rome, was widely read among educated Romans. Generally *Naturales Quaestiones* offered nothing new; it was important only in that it enabled older ideas to be further transmitted.

After Strabo the next "great work" to appear was by Gaius Plinius Secundus (23 A.D.-79 A.D.). He is usually known as Pliny the Elder, to distinguish him from his nephew, Pliny the Younger. Pliny was born in Novum Comum (Como), Italy. Of many works produced by Pliny, only one, the *Historia Naturalis* (37 books), is extant. It is an *encyclopaedia* of nature. In fact, Pliny is the first person to use this term.

Only some of the 37 books are of interest to geographers in general, though Pliny's range of topics is so great that it would be difficult to say just which ones. Book i contains the index and bibliography (citing 473 other authors); ii treats of astronomy and physical geography; iii-vi considers descriptive geography and ethnography (often merely sterile lists); vii is devoted to man (and largely to the fictitious kind); viii discusses land animals (again he related the time-worn fables of fanciful creatures); ix concerns aquatic animals, and since it is based on Aristotle is one of the best books; x, birds; xi, insects and comparative anatomy; xii-xix handle a large variety of essentially botanical matters (including farming and forestry); xx-xxvii deal with medicinal plants; xxviii-xxxii are also concerned with medicine; xxxiii-xxxvii are dedicated to rocks and minerals, and include metals and the uses of these items.

Pliny attempted to sum up all knowledge of the universe, earth, man, plants, animals, and minerals. Actually, he was rather well-equipped to do this. He had travelled widely, serving as statesman or soldier, in Spain, France, Germany, and Syria. He was an avid reader (he says he had read 2000 volumes when he wrote *Historia Naturalis*) and had access to official Roman sources. Much of the value of his work lies in this latter fact, and were his rendering anything better than a dull statistical recitation loaded with fables it might receive a proper hearing among students today. The fanciful digressions of Pliny are in juxtaposition with the science of the Greeks. It makes for a thorough confusion (especially when he makes no chronological distinctions for his sources).

It is a mistake to dismiss Pliny's work with a simple word or two of rejection as some students of the history of geography have done. His contributions are important despite the errors he either perpetuates or creates. His accounts of the Tigris-Euphrates region, for example, are the best of anyone to his time. And, it is Pliny (among others) that Columbus frequently turns to during his voyage to America in 1492.

Pliny's life ended in a most tragic way, on August 24, 79 A.D., when Vesuvius erupted. He actually went to the zone of volcanic activity on

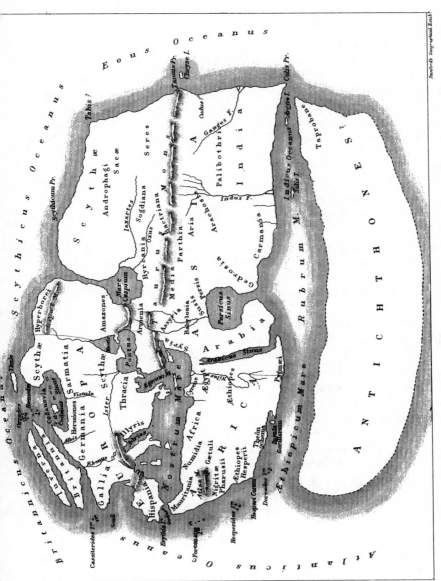

FIGURE 3.2. Mela's World Map

Used with the kind permission of John Murray, Publishers Ltd., London.

the shore of the Bay of Naples to assist the people there and to calm their fears. During the night, while attempting an escape, he was overcome by fumes and died near the sea.

At about the time of Pliny, and surely within ten years of his death, there appeared an interesting little book called the *Periplus of the Erythraean Sea*. Its author is unknown, but he must have been a Greek merchant from Alexandria. In essence the *Periplus* contains sailing directions for the Red Sea, Arabian (Erythraean) Sea, Persian Gulf, and refers to India, Ceylon, and possibly China. It was a navigator's handbook of the first order; one of several produced after the expanded trade with India that occurred after the Greek mariner Hippalus discovered how to sail directly to India from southern Arabia (Cape Fartak) by utilizing the monsoon winds.

The importance of the *Periplus* lies in the fact that it was one of the most exact documents produced in antiquity. Many of the major writers (such as Pliny and Claudius Ptolemaeus) had references of this sort at their fingertips. They did not, unfortunately, use this one. The anonymous author was one of the first to recognize that the east coast of Africa continued to the south, and not to the west as previous (and many later) writers thought. He was also familiar with Africa as far south as Zanzibar (6° S); this at a time when many writers were claiming the "torrid zone" to be impenetrable.

The *Periplus'* composer also understood the trend of India's coasts, something that even later writers failed to comprehend. In addition to coasts and harbors, the *Periplus* furnishes us with an assortment of other interesting and factual items. Included is a discussion of tidal bores, peoples, governments, and items of trade and regions of production.

The time between Pliny and Claudius Ptolemaeus seems to have been one of lost works and anonymous writers. Were it not for frequent citations by later writers much of the lost material would never have come to the surface. Marinus Tyrius (Marinus of Tyre) was one whose work (like that of Eratosthenes) is known to us only through others. His work dates from about the middle of the second century A.D., or a few years earlier.

Marinus' main goal appears to have been to improve upon the existing map of the world. His efforts to achieve this were not in vain, and *almost all new material later incorporated by Claudius Ptolemaeus came from the work of Marinus.* It was unfortunate for Marinus' claim to immortality that he was followed immediately by Claudius Ptolemaeus, who had the ability to arrange the information in a form that not only could be useful but assumed such a scientific pose. It is fortunate, however, that Ptolemaeus borrowed so heavily: his work survived. And

Ptolemaeus should be commended for acknowledging the work of his predecessor.

Claudius Ptolemaeus (hereinafter called "Ptolemy," but unrelated to Ptolemy I, mentioned in Chapter 2) was probably born in Ptolemais, Egypt (26°30′ N, 31°40′ E), about 75 A.D. and died in about 153 A.D. Though the dates of his birth and death are not precisely known, they are within a few years of the truth. Most of Ptolemy's work was produced between 127-150 A.D. at Alexandria.

He is most noted (to geographers) for his *Guide to Geography* (*Geographike Huphegesis*), composed of seven books. Book i is a general introduction and certain astronomical calculations (mostly from Marinus of Tyre). A great amount of the latter part of book i is devoted to maps and map projections. Books ii-vii are made up mainly of lists of places by latitude and longitude. Many maps accompany the *Guide* and they are sometimes thought of as forming an eighth book. Ptolemy does not concern himself with descriptions of countries and their inhabitants, physical features, or products.

Ptolemy took up where Marinus and Hipparchus left off, that is, to make a better map of the world. His map (Fig. 3.3) is convincing proof that he succeeded. He restored the Caspian Sea to its landlocked position, but he had the same confused notion about the east African coast, and he accepted 18,000 miles as the value of the earth's circumference. Regardless of the errors, his was the most scientific map yet produced. And it was to remain the standard until the fifteenth century.

Mention should be made of Ptolemy's work in astronomy and mathematics, both of which had an important influence on certain aspects of geography. *The Mathematical Collection* (*He Mathematike Syntaxis*), after an Arabian translation in the ninth century, is usually known to us as the *Almagest*. It is composed of 13 books and contains, among other things, an outline of the geocentric system, solar and lunar motions, length of the month and year, planets (comprising five books of the total), stars (1022 are listed), precession, eclipses, and methods for making a celestial globe and an astrolabe. Much of the work rests on Hipparchus, and it was the basic work down through the ages until Copernicus. Ptolemy's work *Analemma* offers additional material on the construction of projections (the orthogonal); the stereographic is discussed in his *Planisphaerium.* Further, he wrote treatises on the calendar, weather, mechanics, music, and optics. His knowledge of this latter subject (optics), coupled with the identification of mountains (perhaps Kilimanjaro and Kenya) on his map as *Mountains of the Moon,* offer the tantalizing possibility that Ptolemy discovered some way to view the

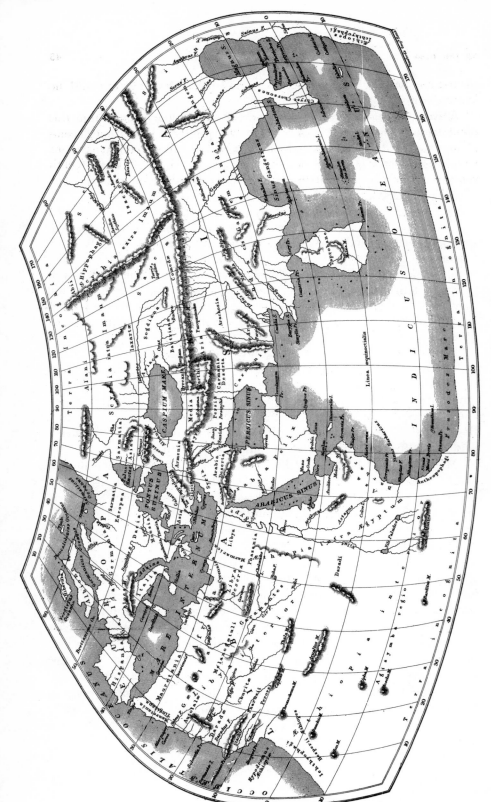

FIGURE 3.3. Ptolemy's Map of the World

Used with the kind permission of John Murray, Publishers Ltd., London.

lunarscape long before the telescope was invented. How else did he know there were lunar mountains?

Ancient geography culminated with Claudius Ptolemaeus: from this point on there was a long decline. After Ptolemy there were some recompilations of existing material, and a few abridgements. Some translations were made into Arabic, or from Greek into Latin. But until the fifteenth century, Ptolemy's world maps were the best man had known.

Chapter 4

The 1000-Year Detour

Rome and Its Aftermath

The decline of the Roman Empire began about a generation after the death of Ptolemy. Usually the fall is considered to have begun at the end of the reign of Marcus Aurelius, or in 180 A.D. The next hundred years were to witness 27 different emperors in addition to dozens who claimed the title. The decay led first to totalitarianism (under Diocletian) and then to the division of the empire (when, in 330 A.D., Constantine established his capital in the Greek city of Byzantium, which he modestly renamed Constantinople).

Christianity became the state religion of the empire in 324 A.D., and, though profiting from the waning power of the state, had little if anything to do with the demise. Contrary to the general notion that geographic thought was repressed by Christian teachings, it had been faltering for more than 200 years. Rome at its mightiest trampled our discipline, and the few bright flames that flickered during those years were Greek-oriented if not Greek-rooted. It is not insignificant to note that it was the Greek spirit (in men like St. Paul) that did not succumb with the empire, and it was the Judeo-Christian tradition that preserved that spirit amid the shambles that was western Europe for centuries to follow.

The city of Rome fell to Alaric in 410 A.D., and the last ruler of the western part of the empire, Romulus Augustulus, was deposed by Odoacer in 476 A.D. The old order was thus destroyed, not at all unlike that of Bronze Age civilization. In fact, many parallels may be drawn between Rome and the Bronze Age. Among the more important ones: both were brought down by "barbarians" (who, nonetheless, had achieved a technology sufficiently high to permit it); chaos followed the collapse of each as new peoples (who had not participated in the old cultures) assumed control; several centuries passed before orderly development was restored; and, the spirit of earlier times was nurtured by those certain few (be they Homers or nameless monastics).

Geography then, along with civilization, took a detour after Ptolemy. But its progress was not stalled, only slowed. This redirection did not lead geography down the dark lanes usually assigned to it. Because the course was altered many historians of geography lost track of our caravan sometime around the second century A.D.

The Byzantine Empire

Between the time of Constantine I and Constantine XI there elapsed 1130 years (324-1453 A.D.). And during this period the Byzantine Empire, first as the eastern division of the Roman Empire and on its own after 476 A.D., had a marked influence on the course of geographic development.

At its height the Byzantine Empire extended from central Turkey to Sardinia, and included much of Italy. Generally it correlates with classical Greek civilization (Fig. 4.1). While western Europe was struggling to rebuild after barbarian invasions and the Roman fall, the eastern empire was forestalling yet other invasions from Asia. It was also perpetuating the Greco-Roman tradition, which resulted in the spread of Christianity throughout eastern Europe and Russia. Accompanying the diffusion of the orthodox faith was the modified Greek alphabet (Cyrillic) adopted by the Russians, Bulgars, and Croats, and the artistic and architectural styles of southeastern Europe.

Between the fall of Rome and the eleventh century, the Byzantine Empire was the foremost power in Europe, economically as well as militarily. The Empire controlled trade in the eastern Mediterranean and to the East and, thereby, was the source for the continuing expansion of knowledge about the world.

A point generally overlooked by the chroniclers of geography's past is this: the Islamic tradition that is credited with picking up the scattered pieces of geography after the fall of Rome rests, to a large degree, on a Byzantium foundation. Islam appears in the seventh century, but its characteristic culture did not emerge for another 200 years. This Islamic culture developed under an influence that was largely Byzantium, Jewish, Nestorian, and Syrian; all of these people derived their culture principally from the Greek. Islamic civilization would not have made its later contributions to our discipline if there had been no Byzantine Empire. Further, the Islamic works that were eventually translated into Latin (including not only those pertaining to geography, but to mathematics, alchemy, and astronomy as well) were produced mainly by Arabic-speaking Jews of Greco-Byzantine origin.

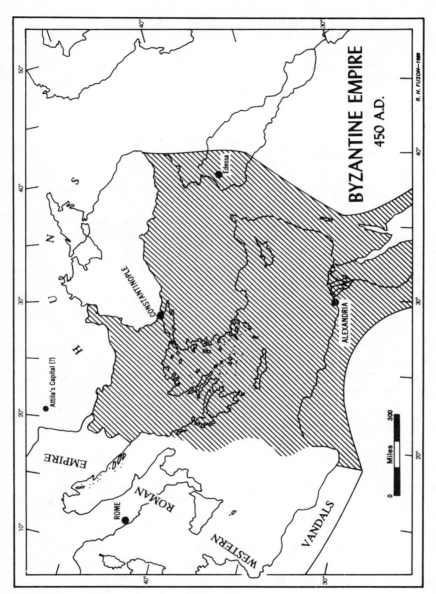

FIGURE 4.1. Byzantine Empire

Constantinople served as a great funnel, pouring ideas into western Europe after the fifth century. Among those listed in A History of Technology[1] are: the astrolabe, armillary sphere, metallurgy, alchemical paraphernalia, architecture, construction, agricultural crops, transport, mining, gun-powder, papermaking, printing, canal-locks, the stern-post rudder, fore-and-aft rig, and the compass.

It is ironic that the ultimate destruction of the empire by the Ottoman Turks (who captured Constantinople in 1453) was aided and abetted by western Christians. There is every reason to believe that had not Byzantium's strength been sapped by 200 years of western interference the empire might have persisted. But in 1204 the Venetian (Fourth) Crusade sacked Constantinople. This band of rabble, financed by the merchants of Venice, paid off the loan for their expedition by reducing Venice's principal trade rival. Weakened by military defeat at the hands of what some historians have called an extension of the barbarian invasions, Constantinople never fully recovered. Within 12 years the Mongols had occupied Kiev and a major link in Byzantine trade vanished. French, Spanish, and Italian looters plagued the coasts for decades. By 1453 a civilization that had successfully defended Europe against Persian, Moslem, and Turk, finally capitulated. The Orthodox Church fled to Moscow for protection, a role Russia has been more than willing to play for over 500 years (though today "protection of the faith" has been modified to mean "protection of all European Slavs," whether Orthodox or not).

The west, however, now had ties with the Near East (and the distrust of the Slavs in the nearer east). For some, however, there had to be an easier way east than through the middle of the Turk and Arab ranks, and those seeking the riches of the Far East were not content to stop in the Holy Land. Some western states were planning an end run, and the world was on the brink of the Voyages of Discovery.

Western Europe

The battered and shattered remnants of the western division of the Roman Empire most assuredly had its problems after Constantine moved east, but the fifth-century disappearance of the state did not mean the end of mankind in these parts. For many (or most) people life continued in much the same way that it had for centuries. The Roman roads remained in operation (though "county" maintenance replaced that of the "federal" government). The farmer farmed the same crops (with the same tools) in the sixth century that he had in the fifth. Law and order

---

[1]A History of Technology, Vol. II, Singer, et al., pp. 758-771.

became a matter of local enforcement (like road building); some feudal lords did a better job than the Romans had done, others did not. Times were not as peaceful, but they were as peaceful as they had been during the earlier Roman conquests. There was decadence, of course. But there was quite a bit during Rome's last 200 years of rule. Though times were changing, the period between the fifth and fifteenth centuries in western Europe is "dark" only to those unwilling to adjust to the different light.

Before we bemoan the destruction of Rome we must remember that most of the world's great civilizations were built upon the ashes of something usually better than the newer one at its outset. Eventually the replacement culture shifted gears and again moved forward. Mycenaen Greece was erased, and Classical Greece eventually emerged. Rome destroyed a whole array of cultures, but became so great we tend to overlook that moral slip. Germanic barbarians drove the native, Christianized, Romanized British into the hills, and eventually created England. The pattern seems rather standard.

Western Europeans clung to more Roman traditions than they discarded. Among these were certain geographical concepts current in the world of pagan Rome; post-Roman Europeans did not invent them. It is patently absurd to blame Christianity for the slower pace of geographic development during the Middle Ages. The Church, more than any other single institution, spawned thought and promoted both trade and travel. The Church did not deny all pre-Christian geographical teaching. St. Augustine (354-431 A.D.), who might be regarded as somewhat of an authority on the subject, *did not* reject the Greek notion of a spherical earth. Even the so-called T-in-O maps (Fig. 4.2), which some have introduced as evidence of geography's decline after Rome, were originally an attempt to show the *sphere* and the lands of both the known and *unknown* worlds. Later T-in-O maps showed only the known hemisphere, but virtually all educated persons of the Middle Ages accepted the principle of sphericity. Further, these maps were mainly adornments for

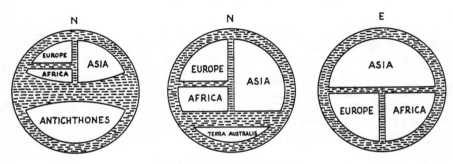

FIGURE 4.2. T-in-O Maps

Courtesy of Imperial Chemical Industries Limited, London.

ecclesiastical and governmental rooms and were not intended for serious study. Some T-in-O maps (like the Hereford map, Fig. 4.3) were much more detailed, but even this map was a large wall map and was designed for decorative purposes.

A word should be said here about the extreme position of a *few* scholars of the early Middle Ages. The one most often cited is Cosmas Indicopleustes (or Cosmas of Alexandria), who flourished in the sixth

FIGURE 4.3. Hereford Map

From: Dickinson & Howarth, *The Making of Geography*, Oxford: The Clarendon Press, 1933. (Used by permission)

century A.D. His work is neither typical nor representative of geographic theory during his time and, therefore, had little influence on later writers.

Cosmas' *Topographia Christiana* (written between 535-547 A.D.) was an attempt to prove that the earth conformed to the pattern set forth in the biblical passages. His universe agreed in every detail with the Tabernacle of Moses. The earth was thought to be flat and rectangular, surrounded by the ocean (Fig. 4.4). Paradise lay beyond the ocean. Heaven was an arch that joined earth at the edges. The sun, much smaller than the earth, revolved about a small mountain in the north.

If the drawings that accompanied the manuscript are the originals of Cosmas, then these are the earliest known examples of Christian cartography.

Political chaos in western Europe lasted until about the ninth century, and the restoration of nominal order generally coincided with incursions

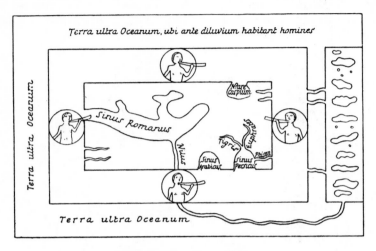

FIGURE 4.4.   Cosmas' Map

From: Dickinson & Howarth, *The Making of Geography*, Oxford: The Clarendon Press, 1933. (Used by permission)

from the north (Northmen) and south (Moslems). Despite contact with these groups, those parts of western Europe not actually under their control pulled themselves up by their own bootstraps. By the ninth century population began to increase more rapidly than ever before, production of both manufactured goods and farm products rose, and times were a little easier than during the early Middle Ages. Some new problems were produced by the changing society. Timber, for example, was becoming increasingly scarce. This fact was felt in the building sector of the economy, and medieval carpenters were seriously affected. Demand often exceeded the supply. The metallurgical industries turned to coal as a replacement for charcoal, and a new source of power emerged. Water power applications took on a new role, and wind was harnessed on a large scale. The latter led to major land reclamation projects (especially in the Low Countries) where pumping had to be continuous.

By the twelfth century Europe was making significant progress. The compass was probably introduced during that century, for the first European mention of it is made in 1187. Near the end of the twelfth century "Arabic" numerals were brought to Europe from North Africa by Leonardo Fibonacci, a merchant of Pisa. This system of place-position numerals, which also included the concept of zero, was derived from the Babylonian, though it may have come to the Arabs from India. The so-called Arabic system was spread throughout Europe when Fibonacci published a description of it in 1201 A.D. Surely, without Arabic mathematics the science that was soon to appear in Europe would have been delayed. The consequences decimal numerals had for geography are obvious. And without the compass there could have been neither the upsurge in mapping and cartography or, more importantly, the Voyages of Discovery.

By 1300 surveying and mapping was an important aspect of medieval life. The first genuine survey map was the Kirkstead Abbey Psalter Map of 1300 (Fig. 4.5). These interesting maps had variable scales;

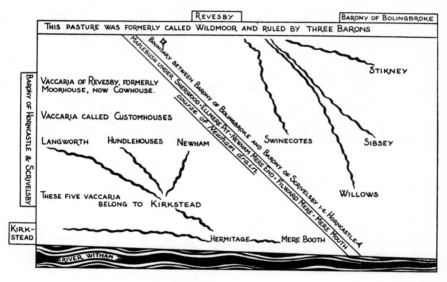

FIGURE 4.5. Kirkstead Map

Courtesy of Peter Janson-Smith Ltd. (for the Province of the Society of Jesus, Beaumont College, Berkshire, England)

important features were exaggerated. Also, east was not necessarily placed at the top as was customary on the decorative maps of the period.[2] Various orientations were used. Such local mapping indicates a concern for the local geography, especially as it pertained to land owner-

[2]The custom of placing east (orient) at the top of a map (hence, to orient) may have its origin in the Near East. In Hebrew scriptures the word *east* and *forward* are the same; *behind* means *west*, *right* means *south*, *left* means *north*. To the ancient Hebrews the Dead Sea was the *forward* (i.e., eastern) sea; the Mediterranean, the *latter* (i. e., western) sea. Early Christian cartographers may have been simply following an earlier tradition. See Aharoni and Avi-Yonah, p. 11.

ship and utilization. In some respects this was similar to the Sumerian activity of three millennia earlier.

By the time of the Kirkstead map the Europeans had developed highly sophisticated sea charts, none of which would have been possible without the compass. One *portolano* map of 1275 A.D. (*Carte Pisane*) is a detailed map of the western Mediterranean. It carries a grid that produces 100-mile squares, and it is the first map to show a proper bar (graphic) scale. Similar maps of this sort culminated in the *Catalan Atlas* of 1375 and eventually evolved into even better *portolano* charts (Fig. 4.6).

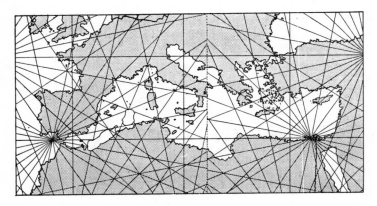

FIGURE 4.6. Portolano Chart

From: Dickinson & Howarth, *The Making of Geography*, Oxford: The Clarendon Press, 1933. (Used by permission)

The European of the late Middle Ages was beginning to expand his knowledge on land as well as on the sea. Epic travels occurred during this time, such as the one sponsored by Pope Innocent IV in 1245. This journey, led by Joannes de Plano Carpini, succeeded in reaching Mongolia by way of east Europe and Russia. Another expedition was sent to Armenia in 1247 by the Pope, and Louis IX (France) sent an emmissary to the Mongols (in Mongolia) in 1253. Perhaps the best known journey was that of Marco Polo, in 1271, though it was his father's second such visit to the Khan.

The revival of Europe that commenced in the ninth century is further indicated by the appearance of universities. By and through these institutions the increasing knowledge of the world could be assimilated and transmitted. Also, many of the great men of medieval Europe are associated with the principal centers of learning. The University of Salerno was known for its medical school by the ninth century; law was important at Bologna by the year 1000, though a true university did not exist until almost 200 years later. A number of other Italian universities emerged during the thirteenth and fourteenth centuries: Vicenza (1204), Padua (1222), Naples (1225), Siena (1241), Piacenza (1248), Rome (1303), Pisa (1343), Florence (1349), and Turin (1400).

Outside Italy the late Middle Ages saw each of the following institutions emerge as a true university (or *stadium generale* as it was called then): Paris (1150), Oxford (1168), Cambridge (by 1209), Toulouse (1233), Salamanca (1243), Lisbon (1290), Orleáns (1305), Grenoble (1339), Valladolid (1346), Prague (1347), Cracow (1364), Vienna (1365), Heidelberg (1385), Cologne (1388), and Erfurt (1389). Many others appeared during this period and additional ones were chartered during the fifteenth century. Though a few of these were founded by royal decree, most of them were chartered by the Pope.

Roger Bacon (ca. 1220-1292), often considered to be the "father" of English science, was a product of Oxford, and taught at Paris and Oxford. His contribution to geography occurs as part of *Opus Majus,* a work he prepared in order to persuade Pope Clement IV to institute reforms in the universities. Actually there was little original in Bacon's work, but his insistence on experimentation and the scientific method was unique in his day. Bacon's geography was largely a restatement of Hipparchus and Ptolemy, and his dream of compiling a vast encyclopaedia of everything known in science is reminiscent of Pliny.

By the fifteenth century Europe was ready to embark upon mankind's greatest period of exploration and population movement. This was in no small part due to the revival of trade and increased political stability. But forces outside Europe "proper" also aided significantly in the preparations. It is necessary to examine these peripheral influences before we return to the mainstream of geographic development.

Chapter 5

By-Passes on the South and North

Moslem and Northman

The arduous detour taken by geography between its classical height (Ptolemy) and the Voyages of Discovery was not the only route open. Post-Roman Europe "proper" was by-passed, to some extent, by lines of development to the south and north. To be sure, there was some interchange among these courses, especially after the eighth century, though in many respects they remained separate. It seems reasonable, however, to suggest that geographical thought could not have climbed upon a new plateau in the fifteenth century had it not been for the eventual merging of the three rather distinct traditions.

The Moslems

Islam, the most recent of the world's great religions, began in 622 A.D., the year Mohammed (570-632 A.D.) fled from Mecca to Medina. Within a century after the prophet's death, Islam had spread through the Near East and into Iran, and had crossed Africa in the north to enter Spain at Gibraltar. The spread into western Europe was stopped in 732 at Tours, France, by Charles Martel, the grandfather of Charlemagne. This savior of western Europe, incidentally, was an illegitimate son of a Frankish nobleman who was able to seize power after being imprisoned by his father's widow. He ruled the Frankish kingdom with an iron hand during the middle eighth century and was rather typical of the "barbarians" that destroyed Rome a few generations earlier. It is indeed ironic that a Germanic tyrant saved the same Europe his ancestors helped tear down!

The Byzantine Empire blocked the Moslems on the east (until 1453), but the new faith pushed into Afghanistan, Pakistan, and central Asia. Eventually it reached down the coast of East Africa and crossed to Malaysia and Indonesia.

56

Moslem culture, as such, really did not exist during the early years (discussed in Chapter 4). It rested on a rather solid Byzantine base, though there were other Near Eastern ingredients. But by the latter part of the eighth century, a few signs of Moslem intellectual curiosity began to emerge.

Harun al-Rashid (766-809) began to encourage the translation of Greek works into Arabic after he became caliph at Baghdad (786). After Harun al-Rashid's reign, his successor, Abdullah al-Mamun (786-833), ordered translations made of Marinus and Ptolemy (among others), and generally fostered the study of both geography and astronomy.

A very important word is appropriate here about the translations of earlier works into Arabic. The early Greek literature (and some Greco-Roman, such as Ptolemy) had been preserved in the eastern (Byzantine) empire. The leading works were translated into Syriac, a branch of the eastern Aramaic Semitic languages, whose center was Urfa (then Edessa), Turkey (37°20' N, 38°45' E). By the end of the second century A.D., Edessa had become a major Christian center and its language grew correspondingly. Eventually, Syriac was a principal (if not *the* principal) language in Mesopotamia and along the Fertile Crescent to Palestine (its pre-Christian home).

The Bible was the first great work to be put into Syriac from the Greek (probably in the second century), and most of the Greek geographical works we have discussed previously were soon translated. This rich literature was readily available in most of the region first conquered by the Arab Moslems. It is sufficiently important that the point be re-emphasized: the Arabs did not create this body of knowledge, or suddenly storm into a library on mainland Greece and carry out the scrolls. They occupied a territory of highly civilized citizens, who possessed the greatest works of the Greco-Roman world. The Moslems discovered no "lost" Greek culture anymore than did the Soviet Union discover books when they occupied Leipzig in 1945 and captured its great library.

The Arabs *did* carry their translations into the western world (especially Spain and Sicily), where they were translated once again (from Arabic to Latin) after the areas were recaptured by the Christians. Most of these translations were made by scholarly Arabs and Jews who remained in the retaken lands. The Arabs' main contributions to geography, other than carrying classical works from the east to the west, were mainly in the areas of measurement and instrumentation, compilations and gazetteers, and travel narratives.

Astronomical observations, made from the Zinjar Plateau near Baghdad, were exceedingly accurate, and for the first time since Poseidonius the circumference of the earth was recalculated. This measurement yielded a latitude degree of approximately 68 miles, a value very close to the truth. Observations were also made from Palmyra (northeast of Damascus) during this same period.

Longitude measurement, destined to remain inaccurate until precise time reckoning appears in the eighteenth century, was conducted with a remarkable accuracy for the period. The Moslems determined the value for the longitude between Toledo (Spain) and Baghdad, for instance, to within 3°. These measurements of longitude were made by comparing the local times of lunar eclipses. Time was determined by means of waterclocks.

Fairly good longitude reckoning, and very good latitude determination (by means of using the back of an astrolabe to compute the mean of the upper and lower meridian transits of a star or by determining the sun's noon elevation), led to the creation of detailed coordinate tables. These tables, however, did not appear until rather late. The first ones (compiled by Ibn al-Zarqali or *Arzarchel*) were done at Toledo in the twelfth century.

In the ninth century a variety of travel narratives and gazetteers began to appear, often accompanied by lists of place names together with their geographic coordinates. Ibn Khurdadbih (a ninth-century postmaster) provided a list of routes and distances, and made certain statements about the earth that were as fanciful as anything the latter-day Romans might have written. He assumed the equatorial region was a desert (because of the heat), and compared the earth with an egg-yolk. He does, however, describe China, Japan, and Korea with greater detail than ever before.

Sometime during the early tenth century Al-Masudi journeyed from Baghdad to China, by way of India and Ceylon. He also travelled through much of the Near East and reached Madagascar, probably by way of the African coast. These sojourns are described in his book *Meadows of Gold and Mines of Precious Stones*.

A number of the tenth-century Moslem descriptive geographies were revised several times. An original by Abu Zaid (in 921) appears in a modified form in 951 (in Istakhri's *Book of Climates*); a third expanded version was published in 977 by Ibn Haukal as *Book of Roads and Kingdoms*. Both Istakhri and Ibn Haukal were travelling merchants who traversed most of the Moslem world during their lives. Ibn Haukal provided us with an example of Moslem cartography (Fig. 5.1), which dispels some of the notion that the Moslems were vastly superior to the Christians in their knowledge of the world.

A contemporary of Ibn Haukal was Avicenna (980-1037), a native of near Bukhara (Uzbek S.S.R.). His principal contribution to the world was in medicine (*Al-Qanun fi'l-Tibb* or *The Canon of Medicine*), not geography, but he was among the first (if not the first) to discuss mountain building by folding, their destruction by erosive forces, and the

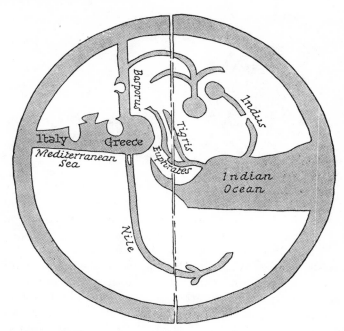

FIGURE 5.1.   Ibn Haukal's Map of the World

From: Dickinson & Howarth, *The Making of Geography*, Oxford:
The Clarendon Press, 1933. (Used by permission)

great length of time necessary for these processes to operate (in *Ash-Shifa* or *The Recovery*).

Idrisi (1099-1154) was born in Spain about 100 years after Ibn Haukal and Avicenna. After an education in Córdoba, he travelled widely through North Africa and the Near East, eventually settling in Sicily. Here he compiled a map of the world for the king (Fig. 5.2), which is an improvement over that of Ibn Haukal, though not by much.

Lastly, let us mention two North African geographers, who number among the most interesting of the fourteenth century Moslems.

Ibn Batutah (1304-1368) was born in Tangier and, like Alexander the Great, set out to see the world at the age of twenty-one. And see it he did; no other Moslem travelled as widely. His journeys eventually carried him to the following places, though not in exactly this order nor during a single trip: Tangier-Alexandria-Cairo-Damascus-Medina-Mecca; Iran-Iraq-Yemen-Mombasa-Mogadishu; Dhofar-Oman-Hormuz-Qatif-Mecca; Egypt-Syria-Turkey-Black Sea-Kaffa-Caucasus-Bulghar-Constantinople; Bukhara-Hindu Kush-Afghanistan-Indus Valley; Delhi-Malabar Coast-Calicut-Gôa-Maldive Islands-Ceylon-Coromandel Coast-Bengal-Dacca-Sumatra-Canton-Kinsai-Peking; Granada-Marrakech-Sahara-Niger-Mali-Ahaggar-Morocco.

FIGURE 5.2. Idrisi's World Map

From: Dickinson & Howarth, *The Making of Geography*, Oxford: The Clarendon Press, 1933. (Used by permission)

This itinerary covered approximately 75,000 miles and provides detailed and accurate descriptions of areas unknown to geography before. While in Turkey Ibn Batutah witnessed the formative stage of the Ottoman Turkish culture. While in Constantinople he spent hours in the company of the Byzantine emperor and former emperor (Andronicus III and II), and his interviews are amazingly complete. Ibn Batutah also was an honored guest of many other rulers, including Mohammed Uzbeg (Mongol Khan of the Golden Horde), the emperor of China, and the king of Mali. His narratives of the latter are virtually the only first-hand accounts extant.

Ibn Khaldun (1332-1406) was a native of Tunis, though his family was from Sevilla. He was widely travelled in North Africa and visited Damascus with the Egyptian Army. His later years were spent in Cairo. Among Ibn Khaldun's many works the most significant to geography is *Muqaddimah* (*Prolegomena*). In *Muqaddimah* Ibn Khaldun offered a scheme of history, whereby he attempted to establish laws for the rise and decline of cultures. His work might be called an example of historical geography with an environmentalist bent. He concluded that arid land produces nomads; arable land produces settled farmers. Nomads are invariably warlike, brave, and prone to occupy a lower stratum of culture than farmers. But though settled peoples develop a higher civilization than wanderers, they tend to decay as their society wallows in its own luxury. This is a pattern that Ibn Khaldun observed within his own Arab Moslem world, which was distinctly on the decline at the time he observed it and formulated his theory of civilization.

Though the Moslem tide (Ottoman Turks, for example) was still far short of its eventual height, the Arab sector of it was ebbing. There were to be no more major contributions to western geographical thought (though much of the Arab work up to this point was not to reach western eyes for almost another century). But while Arab culture was waxing and waning, all was not quiet on Europe's northern frontier.

The Northmen

During the seventh century, a time when Islam was fanning across North Africa and the Near East like a wildfire, there was a stirring on Europe's northside. The movement included several groups of related peoples that we shall collectively call Northmen. Mostly they were Scandinavians, known generally as Vikings, though some (like the Normans) lost this identity and others (like the Angles and Saxons) were never given this appellation. The Irish (and possibly other northern Celtic peoples) contribute to this period, though the name Northmen should not be given them but reserved for the Germanic groups.

Many of the northern Germanic bands were able to move from their culture hearth at the base of the Danish peninsula with impunity after the collapse of the western half of the Roman Empire. Among those of interest at this point were the Angles and Saxons, who went to Britain in the fifth century A.D. and evolved into Englishmen. The Franks moved into northern Gaul and gave that land a new name (France), and leaders like Charles Martel and Charlemagne. The Vandals pushed through France and Spain and across Gibraltar into the Berber territories. Later some of these same blue-eyed Teutons fought for the glory of Islam with the same vigor their name implies. Lombards reached the Po Valley (Lombardy); Visigoths and Suevi took up residency in Spain. Some remained in the vicinity of their origin and were to emerge a few years later as Vikings.

The year 795 A.D. was a most singular year in the north. For one thing, it marks the date of the first Viking attack on Ireland, when they seized Lambay Island (north of Dublin Bay). But not all the Irish were home, for in that same year a group of Irish monks not only discovered Iceland but remained there from February till August. Dicuil, the Irish cleric who described this sojourn in his classic work De Mensura Orbis Terrae (825 A.D.), reported that the monks experienced the almost nightless summer of "Thule" and ventured by boat to the edges of the ice-floes. Dicuil is a reliable source and the visit he depicts might well be the first to that island since the days of Pytheas. He also utilized Roman surveys in his writing and must rank as one of the foremost contributors to geography from this period in northern Europe.

The Icelandic Book of the Settlement (Landnámabók) also records the Irish as arriving in Iceland 65 years before the Vikings. And there is a possibility the Irish reached Greenland before either the Vikings or the

Eskimos. The latter certainly did not enter Greenland from Canada before the eighth century, and passed *through* the Norse settlements during the tenth century on their migration from the west to the east coasts. Erik the Red (who arrived in Greenland in 982) found human habitations in the east and west, and there is a reasonable doubt that not enough time had elapsed for all of these to be of Eskimo origin.

That the Irish were on the move from the late eighth century on there can be no doubt. And right behind them came the Northmen, first to Ireland, then to Scotland, England, and France in the first half of the ninth century.

Serious Viking raids on the Scottish coast began in 802 A.D.; the French coast had sporadic visits in the early 800's and the English coast came under heavy seige in 838 A.D. Paris was attacked in 845, and Hamburg was burned twice, in 851 and 880. Iceland was settled in 860; Greenland, in 986 (though explored by Erik the Red in 982). The Vikings (coming mainly from Denmark at first, and later from Denmark and Norway) spared no one, not even their Germanic first-cousins along the Elbe or their second-cousins in England.

Viking attacks on France continued until the year 911 when the French king, Charles III (the Simple), came to terms with Rollo, the Viking chief. From this beginning came Normandy, when French land passed to the Vikings in exchange for their promise of good behavior and the acceptance of Christianity. Later, the Frenchified Vikings, now called Normans, invaded England in 1066, thereby reuniting two long-separated Germanic peoples.

The Viking forays against England, and the Norman-Viking conquest in 1066, had much to do with the state of geographical knowledge in that land. The activities of the Irish may have also had some bearing on Anglo-Saxon geography, for not only were their wanderings legendary they were, at least in part, based on actual happenings. It is no real surprise that an Anglo-Saxon map of the world (Fig. 5.3), perhaps dating from the late ninth century (and in no case later than the late tenth century), is more sophisticated than maps from other parts of Europe during the same period. The Moslems were never to achieve this level of cartography.

Progress in the north, operating independently from the continent, made remarkable strides. By 1126 Greenland had its own bishop, and it was mapped by the Danish cartographer Claudius Clausøn Swart (called also Claudius Clavus) in the early 1400's (Fig. 5.4). On this map it is interesting to note that Clavus corrected Ptolemy's parallels.

The years between the Viking voyages and 1492 probably produced a number of Atlantic crossings; it is possible that the Irish accomplished one or more crossings and have left accounts of them not unlike Homer's

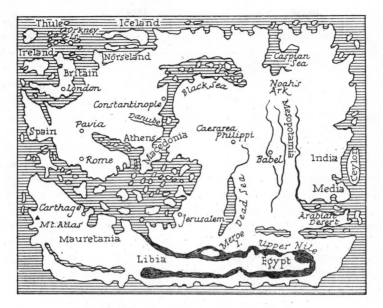

FIGURE 5.3. Anglo-Saxon Map of the World

From: Dickinson & Howarth, *The Making of Geography*, Oxford: The Clarendon Press, 1933. (Used by permission)

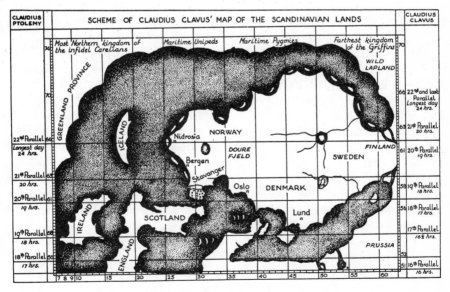

FIGURE 5.4. Claudius Clavus' Map of N. W. Europe

Courtesy of Imperial Chemical Industries Limited, London.

Odyssey. If the Irish did reach America it is understandable why this discovery made no impact on the world. They sought no trade (as did the Phoenicians), or knowledge (as did the Greeks), but simply a retreat in the true monastic meaning of that word.

The Viking voyages are better documented, and some of them did influence the map of the world (Fig. 5.4). Bjarni Herjulfsson was probably the first Viking to reach America, in 987 A.D. While attempting to reach his father's home in Greenland he ventured too far south and seemingly discovered Newfoundland. Sailing south he coasted what was probably Nova Scotia and Cape Cod. His return to Greenland, which he correctly negotiated, became the sailing directions (in reverse order) for Leif Erikson 15 years later. Erikson not only was told of the western lands by Bjarni Herjulfsson (in 1002) but bought Bjarni's ship for the voyage. On September 28, 1003, Leif Erikson landed in the New World, probably at Cape Cod, near Nantucket Sound. After Erikson, an expedition led by Thorfinn Karlsefni spent three years in Vineland. During this sojourn, Karlsefni's wife, Gudrid, bore a son (named Snorri), the first European child born in America. The main geographical fact revealed from this voyage was the first positive reference to the Appalachians.

Several other Viking voyages to the New World occurred after Karlsefni, but the first truly documented journey took place after the Viking period had reached its summit. Henry Sinclair (or St. Clair), a native of Scotland, and Antonio Zeno (of Venice) teamed up under Norwegian sponsorship to venture to Nova Scotia in 1397. The documentation of this trip, in the *Zeno Narrative* (published in 1558), seems indisputable.

During the fifteenth century, but before the first Columbus voyage, there occurred several probable sailings to the New World. The most interesting was a joint Portuguese-Danish expedition to Labrador, from Denmark by way of the traditional Iceland-Greenland route. This expedition involved João Vaz Corte-Real (Portugal) and Johannes Scolvus, Hans Pothorst, and Diderik Pining (all of Denmark), in the year 1472. The voyage is of interest to geographers because it may have been one of the contributing factors to King John's rejection (in 1484) of Columbus' plan to sail west. At the time Columbus was turned down he was told that the Portuguese already had knowledge of the lands to the west, and in 1486 one Fernão Dulmo of the Azores was given a charter to settle *the islands and mainland in the west.*

It is worth noting that Portugal and Denmark were united by marriage (Prince Henry the Navigator's cousin Philippa was the wife of Erik II of Denmark). And there is evidence that Erik II sent Prince Henry copies of Clavus' map (Fig. 5.4) in 1445. Why has history remained silent about a Dano-Portuguese voyage of 1472? The best reason seems to be that such a voyage would have been a closely guarded state secret. Proof of this claim might lie in the fact that Juan de la Cosa drew, in 1500, a map that depicted the islands of the Caribbean with reasonable accuracy, not only giving a good rendering of the *closed* Caribbean coast of Central America but showing Cuba as an island *nine* years before it was officially circumnavigated. It is said that Juan de la Cosa had access to reports of Portuguese discoveries, and that when he went to Lisbon in 1503 he was arrested and detained until he redrew his map, which he then sent to Queen Isabella of Spain. This map incorrectly showed open water in the stead of Central America, which would encourage Spain to keep searching for the passage west.

These actions in the north of Europe, joined only at the end by Portugal, provided a background of geographic knowledge that played no small role in the developments that were to transpire. While Moslem Arab contributions to the south were important to our discipline, they could not be considered of more significance than those made by the Northmen. On one or two occasions the Northerners and Southerners crossed paths: the Normans conquered Sicily, and Idrisi was in the employ of their king Roger, and the Vandals that crossed into North Africa eventually became converted to Islam. Quite clearly the influence of both the north and south was pressing in on the Iberian peninsula by the fourteenth century. This region, long under Roman control (and at an early date colonized by both Greek and Phoenician), appears to be the first to experience an attraction of all these forces. The Moslems and Vikings shared a contemporary rise and decline. Post-Roman Europe (either because of or in spite of pressure from the north and south) recovered. The stage was now set for Europe "proper" to reenter the mainstream of a developing geographic awareness. The detour and its by-passes were about to merge and a new open road lay beyond.

Some Interesting Dead Ends

Indian America, Eskimo,
Orient, and Pacific

Before we move along on the broad, straight road that was the development of geographic thought in Europe after the year 1400, let us pause just long enough to see what the rest of the world was doing. From the standpoint of *theoretical* geography the world beyond Christianity and Islam never accomplished anything worth mentioning; from the *practical* standpoint a great deal was accomplished. Actually, very little theory was produced outside Classical Greece before 1400, and the development of geography to this point was largely in the areas of increased knowledge resulting from travels. This, of course, led to improvements in navigation, instrumentation, measurement, and cartography.

Beyond Europe, North Africa, and the Near East, there were places and times between the Golden Age of Greece and the eve of the Voyages of Discovery that witnessed flashes of pure genius. Some certainly deserve our attention.

The Maya

The Maya thrived as a high civilization between 300 A.D. and 900 A.D.; there was a brief revival from about 1000 A.D. to 1300 A.D. Generally they occupied southeastern Mexico, Guatemala, British Honduras, and a portion of Honduras. The Maya made no maps that we know of, crossed no oceans, discovered no new lands. They did, however, possess the only true writing among the American Indians, and they developed a system of mathematics never matched by Rome. Other than the Maya, only the Babylonians in all of history discovered the concept of the zero.

The Mayan calendar was superior to the one we use now, and their astronomy was of a high order. They developed a variety of calendars (solar, lunar, Venus) based on their astronomical prowess, and possessed highly sophisticated eclipse tables. This information was preserved in books, explained by hieroglyphics, and stored in libraries.

There is a good possibility that the Maya discovered the compass at least 1000 years before it was known to Europe, and possibly before it was known to anyone. Evidence for such a discovery is slim, and conclusive proof still eludes those searching for it. But the Maya did possess magnetite (lodestone) and liquid mercury, and if a sliver of magnetite were ever introduced into a bowl of mercury the Mayans would have had a highly functional compass. There is a tantalizing possibility that the Maya oriented some of their major buildings to magnetic north; this would explain the apparent disorganization of the ceremonial centers. As magnetic variation shifted with time, so maybe did building alignment. If this did occur, the Maya may have been the first major civilization to employ a technique so common to surveyors and planners today.

Little has been said about the humanistic side of geography. Most geographers are ever-awed by nature: its beauty, grandeur, vastness, and harmony. To a large degree the ancient Maya shared this appreciation; they understood their role in the universe, their place in nature. They never destroyed wantonly. Forgiveness was asked when even the earth was marred for farming. They were innate conservationists. Somehow the Maya seem to have a place in our history.

The Aztec

The Aztec civilization of central Mexico was the last of a series of related cultures to occupy the Valley of Mexico. According to their own legends the Aztecs began their wanderings in 1168 A.D. and founded their capital (Tenochtitlán) in the year 1325 A.D. (on the present site of Mexico City).

In many respects the Aztec stage of civilization during the fifteenth century was similar to the Bronze Age of the Old World. Unlike the Maya, Aztec society was dynamic and aggressive. It was a true political state that was rapidly expanding at the time Cortés entered the region in 1519.

Almost unique among the American Indian was the Aztec's interest in maps (though both the Inca and Eskimo also possessed them). To a large degree Aztec mapping was closely related to two basic characteristics of their society: warfare and advanced agriculture.

Warfare, and its accompanying strategy, included not only the gathering of intelligence data but the compilation of maps. Intelligence was usually collected by far-ranging traders, called *pochteca,* who not only obtained valuable goods in trade but served the state admirably as advanced agents. Information gathered by the *pochteca* was assembled and mapped, usually on bark-paper or deer-skin. Colors were lavishly used.

Agricultural practices, especially the creation of new land by filling portions of Lake Xochimilco (south of Mexico City), also fostered mapping. These new lands (the so-called "floating gardens," or *chinampas*) were carefully mapped and obviously planned.

The agricultural (land-use) maps are not unlike those from Sumeria and Babylonia, and they were much more realistic than other classes of Aztec maps (Fig. 6.1). The non-agricultural map was highly decorative. (Fig. 6.2) Its symbolization was naturalistic and pictographic, with scant attention given to relief features. There are many examples of Aztec maps that depict historic events or legendary happenings.

There is some evidence that the Aztecs also engaged in city planning. These cities, with populations as high as 300,000, generally followed a rectilinear plan and appear to have been carefully laid out.

Though Aztec mapping is crude by even the standards of certain other early peoples, the systematic collection of data for the preparation of their maps sets them apart.

The Inca

The Inca culture, occupying the Andean highlands and desert coasts of Pacific South America, was contemporary with the Aztec. And like the Aztecs, the Incas possessed a well-organized, cohesive state that was actively expansive.

The Inca state was divided into quarters, with Cuzco, the capital, in the center. As a matter of fact, the Quechua word for the empire was *Tawantin-Suyo,* or *Land of the Four Parts.* Each quarter was ruled by a viceroy who was a member of the Inca royal family. These quarters were, in turn, divided into provinces, each of which contained 40,000 households. These contained units (tribes) of 10,000 households each, and each tribe consisted of ten units of 1000 households. The units were further divided into two divisions of 500 households; the 500 were divided into five units of 100 households; and, each 100 households was broken down into ten units of ten households each.

Some 6,000,000 people were governed in this manner, and the state kept extremely accurate census records. In all probability, the Inca were more advanced in census-taking than any other American people. Once a border territory was conquered by the central government, a census was the first order of business. The census included people, animals, and crops. This census, along with a *relief model* of the newly-won area (either in clay or stone), was forwarded to the capital. Roads were extended into the annexed region and, if necessary, the entire population

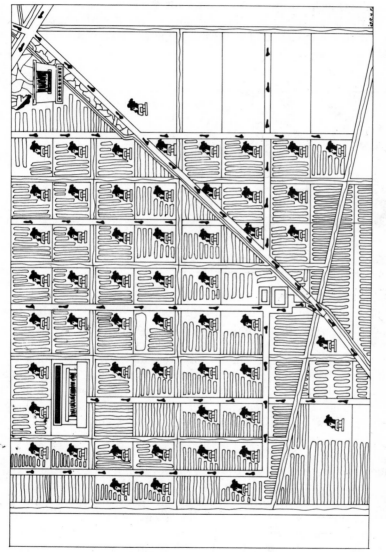

FIGURE 6.1. Reconstruction of a portion of an Aztec map of Tenochtitlán (Mexico City). Causeways are indicated by footprints; canals, by wavy lines. The **chinampas** are shown and certain property lines are indicated.

Courtesy Museo Nacional de Antropología, Mexico City.

was removed to the interior and replaced with loyal Quechua-speaking citizens.

The idea of relief models is unique, though it is somewhat reminiscent of the clay tablets utilized by the Sumerians for the first maps ever made. Inasmuch as the Inca had no writing and only *quipus* (cords, employing knots and colors for meaning) for record-keeping, there were no maps incorporated in books.

FIGURE 6.2. Aztec Map

From: *General Cartography* by E. Raisz. Copyright 1948 by McGraw-Hill Book Co. Used by permission of Mc-Graw-Hill Book Company.

Inca political organization was so effective that it is reasonable to assume that there were many kinds of maps (or models) in use at one time or another. Most of these were probably on clay. The Inca Empire was a socialist state, extremely complex, and tending toward the bureaucratic. But it was this high order of control that made it possible for the Incas to excel in engineering (canals, aquaducts, roads, bridges, tunnels), architectural achievements, agricultural production, textiles, metallurgy, ceramics, and a host of related crafts. Geography played no small part in the organization of this vast empire.

Before leaving the Incas, mention should be made of one practical development that is related to an aspect of geography. The Incas may well have been the first people in history to undertake an effective system of weather control. In order to assure adequate rainfall for their fields on the mountain slopes, Incas would assemble at high elevations above the fields and clouds. From heights of 15,000-17,000 feet they would hurl snow into the clouds below, thus producing rainfall. The technique, as described by the first Spaniards in the area, apparently worked quite well. At last, in the Andes of South America, history produced a people who did something about the weather instead of talk about it!

The Eskimo

The Eskimo's principal contribution to geography has been in the area of cartography, though like all "primitive" peoples they have developed a remarkable rapport with their physical environment. The Eskimo can teach the outsider many fundamental geographic lessons and any student of our discipline should realize and appreciate this potential among non-literate peoples.

But mapping is the one tangible geographic attribute of the Eskimo. Their maps are often considered to be more detailed than maps of the same areas made by Europeans (Fig. 6.3). The map illustrated was

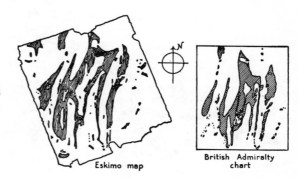

FIGURE 6.3. Eskimo Map

From: *General Cartography* by E. Raisz. Copyright 1948 by McGraw-Hill Book Co. Used with permission of Mc-Graw-Hill Book Company.

Eskimo map

British Admiralty chart

drawn with a pencil and no surveying tools. The accuracy of the mapped area (comprising several thousand square miles) speaks for itself.

Some Eskimo maps consisted of carved bark pasted on a large skin. Again, the accuracy of these bark-and-skin maps (or models) is remarkable.

The Orient

The earliest Oriental map that has survived was made in China in 1137 A.D. (Fig. 6.4). This map, according to Raisz, may have been based on a map of 801.[1] Evidence indicates that the Chinese were actively pursuing geographic information and placing it on maps by the third century B.C. (the first reference to a Chinese map dates from 227 B.C.). Pei Hsiu (224-273 A.D.) is considered by Raisz to be the father of Chinese cartography, and though none of his maps exist his basic rules of map construction have come down to us:[2]

---

[1]Raisz, *General Cartography*, McGraw-Hill, 1948, pp. 6-7.
[2]*Ibid.*

a. Provide a grid
b. Provide proper orientation
c. Show correct distances
d. Show correct relief
e. Show roads correctly

During the third century the Chinese mapped much of Asia, but their knowledge beyond China was extremely limited. There seems to have been a long tradition of local mapping in China, and many maps accompanied detailed geographic descriptions of each province. The Chi-

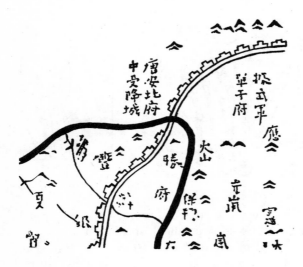

FIGURE 6.4. Chinese Map

From: *General Cartography* by E. Raisz. Copyright 1948 by McGraw-Hill Book Co. Used with permission of Mc-Graw-Hill Book Company.

nese, however, exhibited little interest in regions outside China. The Chinese considered their country to be the center of a flat world, surrounded by barbarians, and probably unworthy of attention. Similar geographic work was going on in Japan and Korea after 1200 A.D., but generally China was ahead in systematic description, census-taking, and "scientific" cartography.

The Pacific

Probably no people in history have surpassed the Pacific cultures in the ability to navigate so much open water with open boats, and to continue this tradition for so many years. The knowledge necessary to populate the Pacific Islands (and Madagascar) from insular Southeast Asia quite obviously existed before any serious voyaging took place. But once in their new island homes the Pacific peoples added to their inventory of skills.

One of the more interesting developments, especially as it relates to geography, was the creation of maps made from the midribs of palm leaves and shells (Fig. 6.5). Islands on these charts were represented by the placement of shells; curved palm ribs indicated the wave fronts approaching the islands. We do not know the date when such charts were first used, but they were generally discontinued about 100 years ago as Western charts spread throughout the region.

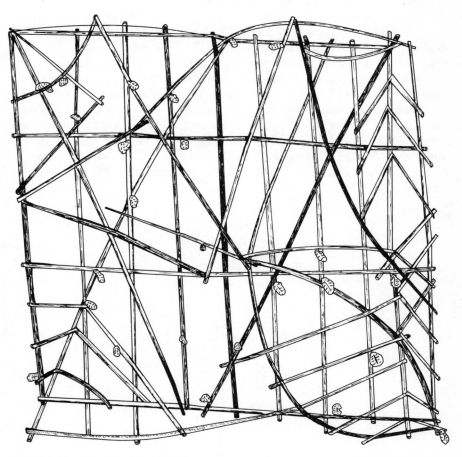

FIGURE 6.5. Sketch based upon a photo of a Micronesian "chart." Curved sticks and diagonals represent wave fronts; shells represent islands.

From: *General Cartography* by E. Raisz. Copyright 1948 by McGraw-Hill Book Co. Used with permission of McGraw-Hill Book Company.

Apparently, the Polynesian, Melanesian, and Micronesian peoples must have been superior navigators, and the possibility that they reached America before the Europeans cannot be totally discounted. It is unfortunate that no written records detail the early navigational techniques.

As with most cultures, mapping usually appears before writing. In a sense, maps are often the only "written" history left to us by some early civilizations. These maps can often tell us a great deal. From them we learn how the population perceived the earth; we learn their geographic awareness. We may also discover many additional facts about the culture from their maps: mythology, history, economy, political organization, technology, and similar things.

Many peoples outside Europe, North Africa, and the Near East were "thinking geographically" before 1400 A.D., but along completely independent lines. Even in China at its peak there was almost a total ignorance of the outside. Most peoples removed from the mainstream of European geographic development were involved with geography at some level, especially if they were agriculturists or seafarers: these occupations seem to require geographic knowledge and skills. Space does not permit a discussion of all the contributions made to the totality of geography by these people, nor does that above do full justice to those mentioned. Suffice it to say that our ethnocentrism should not blind us to the fact that geographic thinking was not unique to the cultures of the Old World.

Chapter 7

The Re-Opened Routes

Portugal and Spain

Geography owes Portugal a great debt. It was this small country, the westernmost of mainland Europe, that brought the Middle Ages to an end and opened the world to mankind for all time. But the price was high as thousands of Portuguese sailors died on voyages to India, Brazil, and Labrador. The great missionary Antonio Vieira was quite correct when he said that God gave his countrymen a small land for their birth-place, but all the world to die in.

But why the sacrifice? Among a multitude of causes underlying the great events of the fifteenth century, one seems to stand out: the desire to reach the Spice Islands (Moluccas). Spices, as strange as this may seem to us in the twentieth century, dominated Europe's economy 500 years ago. At that time, and especially in northern Europe, large numbers of cattle and sheep had to be slaughtered every fall because winter fodder was lacking. *Pepper* was the only answer to the problem of preservation. And the price of pepper in Europe, after the completion of one of the most fantastic trade journeys in all history, was over 10,000 per cent of the original price paid in the Moluccas! Involved in the process were Malay traders, Chinese pirates, Hindu traders, a few tax-hungry sultans, Arab pirates, Arab traders, the ruler of Calicut, Hindu pirates, Arab caravans, Arab desert raiders, many tax-hungry sheiks, the Sultan of Egypt (who collected almost as much as all those that came before), Turkish pirates, and Barbary pirates. The trip through Europe was also plagued with robbers and sundry taxing complications. If the spices ever reached western Europe they were literally worth their weight in gold. No wonder an easy route to the Moluccas was sought by so many.

One man dominated the early Portuguese attempts to find a new route east: Prince Henry the Navigator (1394-1460). Not only does his life closely correspond with the first half of the period when Portugal was a dominant power, but his very existence resulted from an English attempt to aid the Portuguese in their freedom struggle against Castile. The Treaty of Windsor (1386) between Portugal and England followed a victory by those powers over Castile at Aljubarrota the year before. This battle marked the beginning of the modern Portuguese state, and it caused John of Gaunt (Duke of Lancaster and son of Edward III) to be sent from England to assist the Portuguese. The Duke's attempted invasion of Castile was a miserable failure, but his daughter, Philippa, succeeded: she married João I, the king of Portugal. Prince Henry was the son of Philippa and King João I.

Henry launched his attack on the eastern route in 1415, when he (with his father and brothers) wrested Ceuta from the Moors on the other side of Gibraltar. So precious was this African beach-head that Henry was later to permit his younger brother to die at the hands of the Moors rather than give them the city as ransom.

Shortly after the Ceuta conquest, Henry established himself at Sagres, a rocky promontory on Portugal's southwest tip. Here he set up what might be termed western Europe's first oceanographic institute. Scholars from all of Europe were drawn to the windy, salt-sprayed headland: shipbuilders, sailors, navigators, inventors, cartographers (especially Mallorca Jews), and men of letters.

From Sagres the Prince sent forth his fleets, the main objective being the rounding of Africa and the opening of a sea route to the Spice Islands. Some 40 voyages left Sagres between 1419 and 1433, but not one was able to round Cape Bojador (Spanish Sahara). Some benefits, however, did accrue during those years. The Madeiras were rediscovered in 1419 by João Gonçalves Zarco. The Genoese had been there in 1351 (and an Italian map records this voyage); possibly the Phoenicians were there 1000 years earlier. The Canaries[1] were claimed by Portugal in 1420, but Henry was never successful in his attempts to dislodge the Castilians and in 1479 Spanish authority was recognized. Diogo de Silves reached the Azores in 1427, and it is remotely possible that the Phoenicians had also been on these islands at an early date. With the Madeiras and Azores, Henry committed a bold act: he ordered a full-scale colonization. This was an almost unheard-of-thing in the early fifteenth century. In a very few years there was a thriving trade between Portugal and her two pearls in the Atlantic.

But probably the greatest feat occurred in 1433, when Gil Eannes was successful in passing Cape Bojador. This forbidding cape had

---

[1]Pliny called the Canaries, *Canaria* (from *canae* = dogs). He claimed them to be inhabited by packs of large dogs. The Canary island of Hierro (Ferro) was chosen by Ptolemy for his Prime Meridian, which was still in use until the late eighteenth century.

blocked southward navigation for 1000 years; Hanno, the Carthaginian, was perhaps the last to round it. Repeated failures by later sailors to make the passage produced a rich store of legends, many of which were well-founded.

Cape Bojador is a 60-foot high cliff of red sandstone that juts into the Atlantic from one of the most barren mainlands on this planet. Its treacherous main tentacle lies hidden in the shallows, extending 15 miles from the coast. Landslides, frequent along the unstable and unconsolidated coast, dump tons of debris into the ocean, thereby creating the "boiling sea" the ancient mariners feared. The parched land shows no evidence of life. There probably was no better locale if one was looking for an end of the earth. For those brave enough to venture out into the Atlantic to escape the shallows, there was the ever-present risk of being swept to the west by the Northeast Trades through uncharted open seas.

But Gil Eannes conquered the cape. No little credit should go to his vessel, a lateen-rigged caravel. This ship, derived in large part from the east, could sail almost into the wind. Its appearance in the west in the early fifteenth century played a major role in Portuguese and Spanish successes that were to follow.

From Eannes' time forward, the Portuguese made rapid progress in the search for a new route to the east (Fig. 7.1). And with the push southward the Middle Ages came to an end and a new Golden Age was about to emerge. The Cape Verde Islands were discovered in 1460 by Diogo Gomes and Antonio da Nola; Bartolomeu Dias reach the Cape of Good Hope in 1487, and Vasco da Gama reached Calicut in 1498. By 1512 Portugal had reached Sumatra, Java, the Philippines, and the Moluccas. Traders were in Canton in 1516, and in 1530 Portugal had established an embassy in Peking. Much of the new information was being sorted and evaluated by a new breed in Europe: the scientific cartographer (discussed later).

Spain made its move with Columbus (1451-1506), whose four voyages to the New World are too well-known to discuss here. In a sense Columbus was the bridge between Portugal and Spain. He had first gone to Portugal in 1476, arriving in a most ignominious manner: his ship sank and he had to swim the last six miles to shore. From Portugal Columbus sailed to Britain and maybe to Iceland, and down the coast of Africa as far as Guinea. He was married in 1478 to Filipa Moñiz Perestrello, whose father was the Italian navigator that had discovered one of the Madeiras for Prince Henry. For a time Columbus and his bride lived at Porto Santo, Madeira, and their son Diego was born there. Surely the experience gained as a navigator with the Portuguese provided Columbus with the fund of fact and legend that convinced him of the practicality of a voyage to the east by a route that lay west.

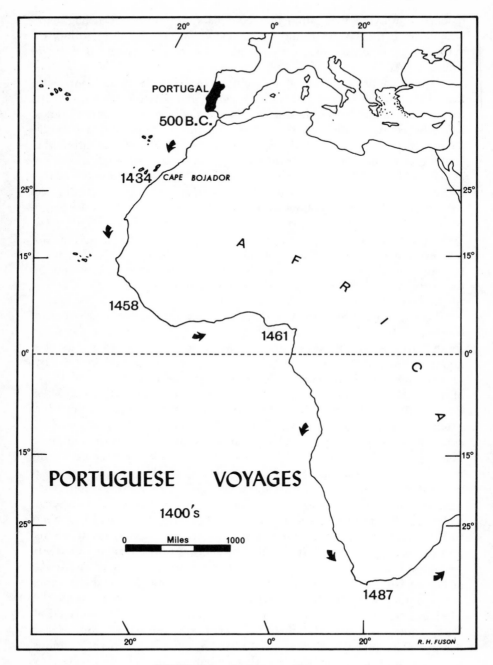

FIGURE 7.1. Portuguese Voyages

Columbus met with no success when he tried to sell his idea to the Portuguese court (it was suggested in Chapter 5 that the Portuguese already had knowledge of western lands). He apparently had also tried to convince both Genoa and Venice that the voyage was feasible. While Columbus was in Spain, trying yet another approach, Dias reached the Cape of Good Hope, accompanied by Columbus' brother, Bartolomé. Upon the return of this expedition to Portugal, in December, 1487, Columbus hurried to Lisbon to consult with his brother. Christopher went back to Spain to try again, while Bartolomé hustled off to England to see if Henry VII might care to sponsor such a venture. The latter failed, but Christopher's patience was eventually rewarded.

The known world, in 1492, is preserved for us from a globe made by Martin Behaim of Nuremberg, Germany (Fig. 7.2). It is readily appar-

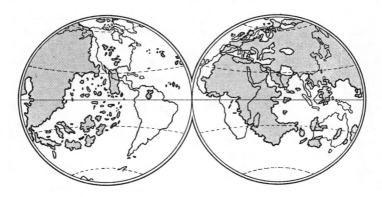

FIGURE 7.2. The World According to Martin Behaim

From: Dickinson & Howarth, *The Making of Geography*, Oxford: The Clarendon Press, 1933. (Used by permission)

ent that the Ptolemaic tradition continued to exert a strong influence among European cartographers on the eve of the Voyages of Discovery. Perhaps it is fortunate that Columbus, as Behaim, accepted the value of 18,000 miles for the earth's circumference, and the placing of certain off-shore Asian islands at about where Mexico actually lies. Had the true distance between Europe and Asia been known (while knowledge of an intervening land-mass remained unknown), there is little chance that Columbus would have attempted to cross so much open water.

After the epic voyage of Columbus came a profusion of explorers. But the greatest voyage of them all, perhaps surpassing even that of the Admiral of the Ocean Sea, occurred between 1519 and 1522. For it was Ferdinand Magellan that finally proved, in a manner that everyone could understand, that the earth was truly a sphere.

Magellan, like the Italian, Columbus, was a foreigner in Spain. And, again like Columbus, he had been rejected by the Portuguese crown when he petitioned his case. Perhaps leaving Portugal was a greater disappointment to Fernão de Magalhães, a native of that country, than it was to Columbus, but leave he did and much to Spain's delight.

Magellan shared another bit of fateful similarity with Columbus: his whole voyage was based on a geographical misconception. Magellan had obtained (in 1515) the log and charts of one João of Lisbon, a rather obscure Portuguese navigator who had sailed along the South American coast the previous year. During the voyage João sailed into the Río de la Plata for over 100 miles, and returned to Portugal with the conviction that he had discovered a strait to the ocean beyond. Magellan set out for this passage and the Spice Islands beyond. Though he died in the Philippines, one of his five ships (the *Victoria*) returned to Sevilla. Of the 268 men who had departed Sevilla's "Dock of Mules" three years earlier, only 19 returned. One of them, Juan Sebastián del Cano (sometimes Elcano), captain of the *Victoria,* is usually credited with being the first man to circumnavigate the globe in a continuous voyage (though 18 others also accomplished the feat). His name is preserved in the famous Spanish geographic society *Instituto Juan Sebastián Elcano*. Perhaps some credit should go to Magellan's Malaysian slave, Enriques ("Malaccan Henry"), whom the navigator had brought to Portugal from the East Indies in 1505. Enriques was probably the first man to physically travel around the world.

Portugal was on the wane by Magellan's time. Two of history's greatest blunders (the rejection of Columbus and Magellan) had caused the Spanish flag to be planted not only across the Atlantic, but on both sides of the Pacific. Portugal was overextended: the country had neither the physical nor human resources to maintain its role. It is indeed ironic that the little nation that had discovered so much of the world virtually ceased to exist by 1580, when it came under Spanish rule for 80 years.

The world was made truly known, then, by Portugal and Spain. Legend and myth gave way to fact. And these facts were among the threads that would soon be woven into the fabric we call modern geography.

Chapter 8

The Modern Hearth Established

Northwestern Europe

By the beginning of the sixteenth century there appeared in Germany a neo-Greek revival of theoretical, mathematical, and descriptive geography. It is not easy to date this precisely, nor is it possible to fully explain why Germany became the locale for the formative development. The reasons underlying Germany's entry into the geographic mainstream are largely historic, and are far too complex to analyze here. But a few events must be mentioned.

Hapsburg rule came to an end in 1493. The 220-year reign of this dynasty was especially marked in the later years by peasant revolts, feuds among the nobility, and general social chaos. Even so, German technology was on the rise, and the invention of *printing* alone might have given Germany an edge over its competitors for geographical pre-eminence.[1] Further, Maximilian I (who ruled from 1493-1519), aptly dubbed by some as "the last knight," brought imagination to the court. And through the marriages of his children there was forged a chain that connected parts of Germany, Spain, the Netherlands, and Austria.

The Reformation began during Maximilian's time, and long-standing religious unrest reached a climax on October 31, 1517, when Martin Luther nailed his 95 theses to the door of the palace church. Again, the role of printing emerges, for without the widespread distribution of Luther's call for a debate there may well have been no Reformation, at least not then.

Maximilian I was succeeded by his grandson, Charles I of Spain (known as Charles V after succession). Charles came to Aachen in 1520 to be crowned, leaving Spain in a state of revolt. And after presiding at the diet of Worms (1521), Charles left Germany to reconquer Genoa

---

[1] A printing office was in operation in Mainz in 1447. The connection with the East is hazy, but a book was printed with metal type in Korea in 1409.

and Milan. By the time he returned to Germany, Lutheranism had become a national movement and the Reformation was in full swing.

Geographical reform closely paralleled religious reform. The first stages of the changing geography were, as we have seen so often, of a cartographic nature. Nuremberg, a center for precision instrument manufacture, became the focal point. Martin Behaim and his globe of 1492 have already been mentioned (Chapter 7). Behaim's teacher (Regiomontanus) was a pupil of Peurbach, generally agreed to be the father of fifteenth-century German cartography. The ephemerides, published at Nuremberg by Peurbach and Regiomontanus, were used by Columbus.

To another cartographer of this period goes credit for putting *America* on the map, though it first appeared on a globe in 1507. Martin Waldseemüller, professor of cosmography at St.-Dié (now in the Department of Vosges, France), assigned this name to what we now call South America, though on his globe it was separated from North America by water.

Road maps (itinerary maps) became increasingly important during this period. Waldseemüller published such maps in 1511 and 1513, but examples of these maps date from at least the mid-1400's. A traveler's pocket compass-dial was created by the Nuremberg craftsmen to accompany the road maps, and distance and direction began to be treated with some degree of precision.

The rapidly expanding knowledge of the world stimulated the cartographers. Contarini (1506) and Ruysch (1508) modified Ptolemy's conic projection, and Johann Werner (1514) produced not only a heart-shaped world map but made the first true stereographic projection. The improvement of world maps caused a corresponding improvement in regional maps. A map of the Rhineland, on a scale of about 1:500,000 and probably the work of Waldseemüller, has all points correct to within 18' of latitude, and azimuths are within a few minutes of accuracy.

By 1533 Gemma Frisius, a mathematics professor at Louvain, had demonstrated the principle of triangulation; plane-table surveying was described 18 years later by Abel Foullon. At about the same time (and not later than 1558), Leonard Digges of England gave the world the theodolite.

German theoretical geography during the sixteenth century is best represented by Peter Apian (or Peter Bienewitz) and Sebastian Münster. Apian's work in mathematical geography and astronomy became the standard work for the next hundred years, while Münster's descriptive geography was the first such significant work produced by a German.

Apian's work was all done in the sixteenth century (he was born in 1495), and his greatest contributions were *Astronomican Caesarem* and *Cosmographicus Liber*, both written when he was about 28 years old.

Apian, like Ptolemy, distinguished between chorography and geography; the former could be considered a regional description; the latter, a worldwide description.

Münster (1489-1552), first a Franciscan and later a Lutheran, was foremost an Hebraist. He was a professor of Hebrew and the first German to edit the Hebrew Bible (1534-35). He is known to our discipline, however, for *Cosmographia* (1544). This great work is essentially a regional geography of the world, but the emphasis is on Germany. Some attention is given earthquakes, erosion, rocks and minerals, and related items. This monumental work, like Apian's, became the standard for a century, and 40 editions appeared in Germany alone.

After Münster's death in Basle (of the plague), the nerve-center of geography shifted to the Low Countries. The Dutch-Flemish influence was to last for about 100 years. As during the latter period of German domination, two men stood out among the Dutch-Flemish group: Gerhard Kremer (Mercator) and Abraham Wortels (Ortelius).

Mercator (1512-1594) was probably the greatest of all sixteenth-century geographers. He studied at Louvain under Gemma Frisius, taking courses in mathematics, astronomy, and cosmography. He also became skilled at making precision instruments. Mercator served Frisius as an engraver, and was so skilled that Charles V had him make a set of surveying instruments. Fear of religious persecution (he had been arrested for embracing Protestantism) forced Mercator to abandon Louvain for Duisburg, in the Rhineland. Many maps were produced by Mercator at Duisburg, including one of Europe in 15 sheets and one of the British Isles in eight sheets. His greatest achievement came in 1569 when he published his famous world-map under the title *Nova et aucta orbis terrae descriptio ad usum navigantium accommodata* (Fig. 8.1).

Mercator broke with the Ptolemaic tradition with this map. For one thing, he selected a new prime meridian, abandoning Ptolemy's Fortunate (Canary) Islands meridian for one through the Azores. This latter one, felt Mercator, was closer to the point where magnetic variation shifted from easterly to westerly, and therefore was a good place to divide the world. Mercator also gave up the idea of the conic projection, which worked well for a small portion of the earth but has no value for the earth as a whole. And, his new map gave true bearings (rhumb lines) between any two points while preserving shapes (the property of conformality). The earlier *plain charts* kept north-south distances true, but exaggerated east-west distances. Mercator, in exaggerating north-south distances as well as east-west ones, made it possible to plot a ship's course with a straight line.

Mercator's map (of which only an outline is shown in Fig. 8.1) still carried many erroneous place-names, inherited from Ptolemy, Marco

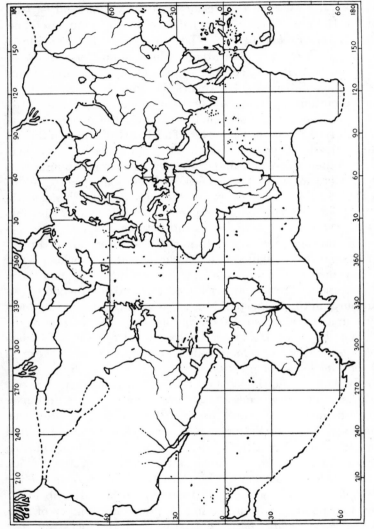

FIGURE 8.1. Mercator's Map of 1569

From: Dickinson & Howarth, *The Making of Geography*, Oxford: The Clarendon Press, 1933. (Used by permission)

Polo, and a multitude of other sources. But it was to free cartography from a tradition that had shackled it for over 1000 years.

Just before Mercator died he began work on an atlas, which was completed by his son, Rumbold, in 1595. Mercator appears to be the first cartographer to ever give the name *atlas* to a collection of bound maps. And he served as an inspiration for many who followed.

Abraham Ortelius (1527-1598) was born in Antwerp. He was trained as an engraver and later sold maps and antiques. As a businessman he became a friend of Mercator and, in 1560, tried his hand at map-making. Ortelius produced many maps, but became famous for his epic atlas, *Theatrum orbis terrarum* (*Theater of the World*), published in 1570. The atlas originally included 70 maps, but he added 17 more in 1573, and continued to add maps for five more editions. This work was a tremendous success and achieved world-wide acclaim for its author. Largely on the fame obtained by this exceptionally scholarly work, Ortelius was appointed geographer to Philip II of Spain in 1575. The influence of Mercator is readily seen in Ortelius' map of 1570 (Fig. 8.2).

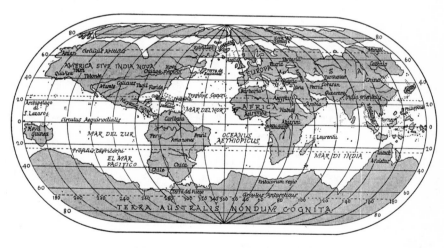

FIGURE 8.2. Ortelius' Map of 1570

From: Dickinson & Howarth, *The Making of Geography*, Oxford: The Clarendon Press, 1933. (Used by permission)

Others that followed Mercator included the brother-in-law of Mercator's son: Jodocus Hondius (1563-1611) made a world map in 1595, the first to depict Drake's round-the-world voyage of 1577-80. Edward Wright (1558-1615) published the first English example of a map based on the Mercator projection in 1600 (Fig. 8.3). He scrupulously avoided depicting unexplored areas (note Australia and western North America).

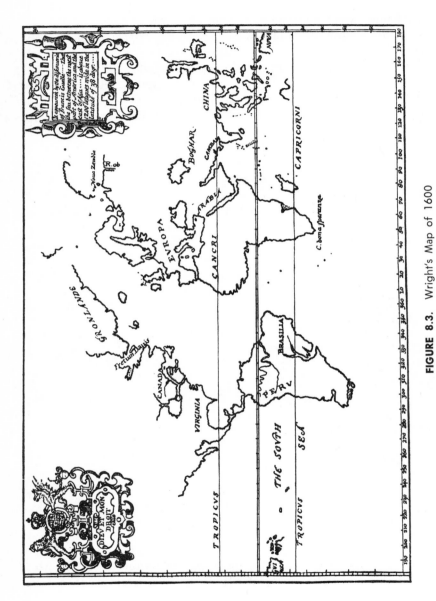

FIGURE 8.3. Wright's Map of 1600

From: Dickinson & Howarth, *The Making of Geography*, Oxford: The Clarendon Press, 1933. (Used by permission)

Wright also was the first (in 1599) to provide a set of mathematical tables by which the Mercator parallels could be spaced (Mercator had not made this information public). In fact, the Mercator chart did not become generally accepted until Wright (assisted by Thomas Harriot) drew up these tables.

By 1600 the British and Dutch explorers had wrested the lead from the Spanish and Portuguese. The list of explorers who contributed to the expanding knowledge of our planet in the 1600's is almost endless. But though the world was rapidly becoming known by the seventeenth century, there had yet to be a truly comprehensive geography covering mathematical and physical on the one hand, and regional description, based upon the new discoveries, on the other.

Philip Clüver (Cluverius), a German, attempted to accomplish the task of writing the first comprehensive, modern geography. In 1624, two years after his death, Cluverius' great work, *Introduction to Universal Geography*, appeared. He had published an earlier work (*Germania Antiqua* in 1616) that was essentially historical, and was writing another (*Italia et Sicilia Antiqua*) when he died in 1622. Like Herodotus and Strabo, Cluverius was in the beginning an historian, and turned to geography afterward in order to provide a proper foundation for historical understanding. *Universal Geography* consists of six parts: one is concerned with the whole earth; the other five are regional descriptions. His physical geography leaves much to be desired and his ideas are those current during the preceding century. His regional geography, however, steeped in history, is excellent for its time.

A year after Cluverius' famous work, Nathaniel Carpenter brought forth the first scientific geography written in English (*Geography delineated forth in Two Bookes*, 1625). Carpenter, like Cluverius, saw a two-fold division of geography: *spherical* (mathematical and physical), and *topical* (areal relationships of phenomena). His regional (topical) treatment was inferior to Cluverius, and the latter's work became the standard for the next hundred years. Carpenter's physical geography was reasonably good, but it was so greatly overshadowed by Varenius' work that it soon lost any significance it might have once had.

Bernard Varenius (1622-1650), born Bernhard Varen, in Hitzacker (near Hamburg), Germany, was one of the truly great geographers of all time. Had he not died a premature death at the age of 28 years, he may well have become the most famous of all pre-modern geographers. A very good case could be made that Varenius *was* the father of modern geography.

His two great works were *Descriptio Regni Japoniae* (1649) and *Geographia Generalis* (1650). The former consists of five parts: a description of Japan, a description of Thailand (which was a translation of Schouten's work), a discussion of Japanese religion, notes on African religions (taken from a work by Leo Africanus), and a short section on various countries in general.

The *Descriptio Regni Japoniae* was an example of what Varenius called "special" geography. Today this is termed "regional" geography. *Geographia Generalis* was concerned with what we know today as "systematic" geography. It is interesting to note that Varenius believed that regional geography was taught at the expense of systematic geography, and that is why geography had a difficult time winning its proper place among the sciences. Generally he felt that regional geography (as taught during his time) was not worthy of being called a science.

General (systematic) geography was divided by Varenius into three sections: *Absolute* (earth form, land, water, mountains, forests, deserts, atmosphere); *Relative* (latitude and longitude, climate); *Comparative* (an interpretation of those things which arise from comparative studies).

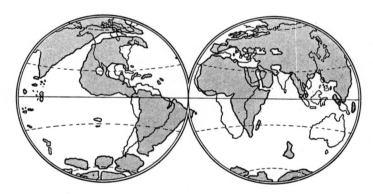

FIGURE 8.4.   Schoner's World Map—1523

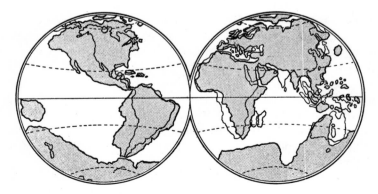

FIGURE 8.5.   Mercator's World Map—1587

From: Dickinson & Howarth, *The Making of Geography*, Oxford: The Clarendon Press, 1933. (Used by permission)

Special (regional) geography also was divided into a three-fold system: *Celestial* (climate and astronomy); *Terrestrial* (shape, size, location, boundaries, mountains, rivers, forests, deserts, soil, animals, minerals); *Human* (people, arts, trade, culture, language, government, religion, cities, places).

The sections of *Geographia Generalis* that treat of mathematical and physical questions are almost modern. His ideas and understanding were far ahead of their time. Had Varenius lived, and assuming he had continued to be as productive throughout his active life, there is no telling what impact this seventeenth-century geographer might have had on the development of the discipline. It is reasonable to assume that his influence would have been monumental.

For the next 100 years after Varenius (between 1650 and 1750) there was very little written in either descriptive or systematic geography. This was a period of consolidation. It saw significant advances made in

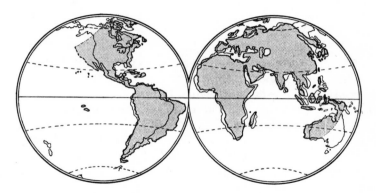

FIGURE 8.6. Homan's World Map—1716

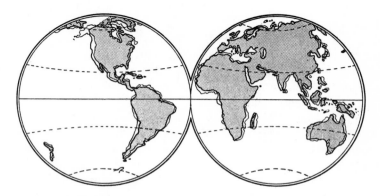

FIGURE 8.7. D'Anville's World Map—1761

From: Dickinson & Howarth, *The Making of Geography*, Oxford: The Clarendon Press, 1933. (Used by permission)

the fields of measurement and cartography. Instruments were improved, though few new ones appeared. Galileo's telescope was invented before Varenius (in 1611) and John Harrison's chronometer (which finally provided a method for accurate longitude determination) was completed in 1759.

The mid-seventeenth century marked the establishment of several famous institutions. The Royal Society of London (for Improving Natural Knowledge) was founded in 1660, and was to sponsor many important projects. The French Academy of Sciences was established in 1666. The Royal Greenwich Observatory dates from 1675, and a Board of Longitude appeared in England in 1713 (which published the first *Nautical Almanac* in 1767).

Cartography reached remarkable heights by the seventeenth century, a field dominated by the French at that time. William Delisle (1675-1726) produced, in 1700, the best world map ever made up to that time. But even Delisle's great achievement was surpassed by J. B. B. D'Anville (1697-1782). His *Atlas General* (1737-1780) became a classic, and during his lifetime he produced more than 200 maps of the highest order. Figures 8.4-8.7 vividly illustrate the changing knowledge of the world between 1523 and 1761, and D'Anville's map is essentially modern in every detail. D'Anville mapped only things that were proven to be factual. Unsurveyed interiors were left blank.

By 1783 J. G. Lehmann had combined contours and hachures to produce the first good relief (though contours were used for depths by M. S. Cruquius in 1728, and hachures were used as early as 1674 by David Vivier). Between 1734 and 1744, French geodetic expeditions, operating in Peru and Lapland, confirmed Newton's theory of polar flattening and equatorial bulge. Thus the true shape of the earth was closely approximated.

After 1750 there was need once again to take stock and pull together all of the rapidly accumulating data. A number of works appeared in England, France, Germany, and Sweden. As a fitting culmination to the eighteenth century, one man should be singled out, for he provides the bridge between the still-physical geography of the eighteenth century to the more modern approach of "man on the land" that is about to appear in the nineteenth century.

Immanuel Kant (1724-1804) was born in Königsberg (Kaliningrad), East Prussia (now USSR). Virtually all of his life was spent in Königsberg, where he attended school and later taught at the university. His university career began in 1755 (as a non-paid lecturer), and continued almost up until his death. In 1770 he became professor of logic and metaphysics. Kant's output of scholarly writings was enormous, and his contributions to geography comprise but a minor part of the whole.

Nevertheless, Kant taught geography at Königsberg for 30 years, and most of these lectures were published. His position and reputation permitted him to secure for geography a firm position within the framework of contemporary philosophy. To Kant, all knowledge could be classified under one of the following schemes: *systematic sciences* (disciplines that study categories, such as zoology studies animals); *historical sciences* (the study of facts and their relationship through time); *geographical sciences* (the study of facts and their relationship in space). Kant expressed the idea that physical geography is the "summary of nature" and the foundation for all other forms of geography. Regardless of the validity of Kant's system, geography from that point forward won its rightful place among its sister disciplines. In no small measure, Immanuel Kant set the stage for the modern period that was just dawning on the horizon.

Chapter 9

The Modern Hearth Developed

Northwestern Europe

Modern geography was born in Germany during the first half of the nineteenth century. It was a culmination of the long evolution that we have traced from the East. The new geography, and the new breed of men that directed its course, was able to emerge because of three principal reasons: (1) exploration had proceeded to a point where the physical and cultural world could be discussed intelligently (and there was a dramatic push during the nineteenth century to complete this exploration); (2) measurement, surveying, and cartography had progressed to the point that they had become truly scientific; (3) progress in other disciplines enabled the geographer to draw on an ever-increasing amount of accurate data.

The reader may have felt, to this point, that an inordinate amount of space has been devoted to the first two points cited above (exploration and mapping). But scientific geography is absolutely and inextricably bound to them. It was not until the nineteenth century that the geographer's laboratory was ready for business (Fig. 9.1). And two men were ready to put the facilities to full use.

The first half of the nineteenth century was the *Age of Humboldt and Ritter*. Though there were other geographical practitioners between 1800 and 1859, they were dwarfed by these two giants.

Baron Friedrich Heinrich Alexander von Humboldt (1769-1859) was born in Berlin of a noble family. He was educated at the University of Göttingen and the Freiburg Mining Academy, and until 1796 he served as an assessor and later director of mines for the Prussian government. During his time in mining Humboldt investigated basaltic rocks, underground flora, magnetic declination in rocks; and instituted social reforms in the mining industry.

By 1796 Humboldt had probably already committed himself to a geographic career, but he was unable to travel extensively until after

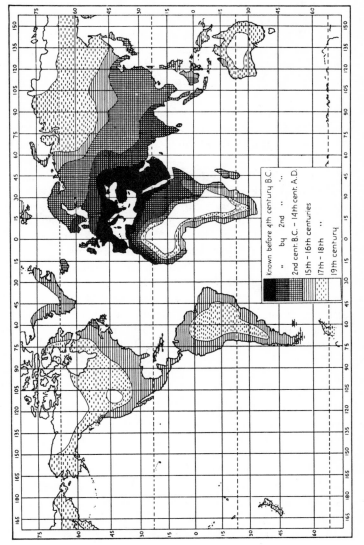

FIGURE 9.1. The Progress of Exploration

From: Dickinson & Howarth, *The Making of Geography*, Oxford: The Clarendon Press, 1933. (Used by permission)

his mother's death in that year. Earlier, while at Göttingen, Humboldt had met Georg Forster, who encouraged the study of geography. Forster may be credited with turning Humboldt to a geographic life, for his influence was profound. During Cook's second voyage around the world Forster had served as a close friend and companion of the captain, and in 1778 Forster attempted to relate man and his environment in a book titled *Voyage Around the World*. Humboldt made one journey with Forster to the Rhineland, Netherlands, England, and France during his university years, and the thrill of field research was forever implanted in his soul.

In 1796 Humboldt went to Paris to join the famous French botanist Aimé Bonpland for a trip to Egypt. They hoped to join Napoleon there, but after reaching Marseilles they changed their plans and travelled to Madrid, where the two adventurers were to remain for three years. The journey that followed earned Humboldt eternal fame.

In 1799 Humboldt and Bonpland went from Spain to the Canary Islands, where Humboldt's observation of a meteor shower eventually led to an understanding of this phenomenon's periodicity. Their next stop was Caracas, Venezuela, and in 1800 they set out to explore the Orinoco River. Some 1700 miles of the great river were covered during a four-month period, and the connection between the Orinoco and Amazon Rivers was established. Humboldt recorded everything he saw in the savannas and jungles of Venezuela. Cuba was the next point visited, but soon the explorers returned to South America, this time via Cartagena, Colombia. The trip through the *Cordillera* to Lima, Peru, was a difficult one, but without serious complications. Humboldt and Bonpland spent some time in Bogotá and Quito, and paused long enough to climb Mt. Chimborazo to almost the 19,000-foot level, and to explore the source of the Amazon.

It was while in Peru that Humboldt studied the adjacent ocean and its associated current (now the Humboldt Current). He also studied the guano deposits and made astronomical investigations. From Peru the two friends moved on to Mexico for a year, then passed through the United States on their way home in 1804.

During the next four years Humboldt went to Italy to investigate Mt. Vesuvius, then returned to Berlin where he occupied his time writing (*Ansichten der Natur*, 1807). In 1808 he returned to Paris, where he worked for 19 years on the materials he had collected during his five-year sojourn with Bonpland. Though Humboldt's South American work was never completed, it eventually totaled 29 volumes and contained 1425 maps and plates. Virtually every aspect of natural history was covered, as well as a full treatment of human and economic questions.

Space does not permit a listing of all the works of this great man. In meteorology he introduced the use of isotherms, noted the relationship between altitude and temperature, investigated tropical and mid-latitude storms. In geology he became a leader in volcano research. He wrote the first scientific plant geography and pioneered biogeography (he personally collected 60,000 specimens of plants). He was an expert on magnetism and promoted the first international cooperation for its study (between England and Russia). He traveled widely in Eurasia, going as far as the Chinese border via the Altai Mountains.

Humboldt served in various government posts and participated in every important scientific society in the world. He was one of the founders of the *Gesellschaft für Erdkunde zu Berlin* (in 1833). During the time after 1808, Humboldt was probably the most famous man in Europe (excepting possibly Napoleon Bonaparte). He fought for human rights and dignity (and greatly influenced Simón Bolívar), and forever won a place in the hearts of colonial peoples.

Among all of Humboldt's writings, geographers look principally to one, *Kosmos,* published between 1845 and 1862 (in five volumes). This was his *magnum opus.* It covered every aspect of physical geography and laid the foundation for this branch of our discipline.

Humboldt was primarily a physical geographer, but he also laid the groundwork for systematic regional geography. His descriptions of Mexico, Cuba, and the Orinoco region set the pattern for years to come.

When Humboldt died in 1859 he was accorded a state funeral. His active writing ceased only a few weeks before his death at the age of ninety, and though many of Humboldt's scientific conclusions have been surpassed, Broek observes that his "vivid descriptions of landscapes, nourished by sensitive and perceptive observation, remain among the best of their kind in geographic literature."[1]

Carl Ritter (1779-1859) was Humboldt's contemporary. Though they shared many things in common, the two men were at the same time quite unalike.

Ritter was born in Quedlinburg (near Magdeburg), Germany. His father died when he was only six, and the family was left in difficult circumstances (Humboldt was relatively wealthy). Ritter's early training followed the system of Rousseau, stressing conformity to natural law. He later entered the University of Halle, studying botany, mineralogy, history, physics, and chemistry. He supported himself primarily as a tutor but was publishing in geography by 1804. A regional geography of Europe published in that year received excellent reviews. In it he ex-

---

[1]Broek, p. 22.

pressed the opinion that geography and history were inseparable and that man influences nature and nature influences man.

Ritter met Humboldt in 1806, and from that time forward the two men became fast friends, and were in close contact with one another after 1827 when they were both in Berlin. Together they were (in 1833) co-founders of the Berlin Geographical Society. Ritter had moved to the University of Berlin to become its first professor of geography in 1820, after serving first at the Frankfort Gymnasium, and earlier at Göttingen. It was while at Göttingen (1817-18) that he published his masterpiece, *Die Erdkunde im Verhältnis zur Natur und zur Geschichte des Menschen* (*Geography in Relationship to Nature and to Human History*). This first volume, on Africa, was part of a long-term project, but, even so, it won Ritter fame. Humboldt praised *Erdkunde* as "the most inspired work of its kind." Humboldt went so far as to intervene in royal circles in order to get Ritter relief from his many duties so that he might devote more time to the forthcoming volumes. The volume on Asia appeared in 1832; six more volumes on Asia were published between 1832-1838; an additional 11 volumes on Asia came out between 1838-1859. The total of 19 volumes (one on Africa and 18 on Asia) fell far short of Ritter's projection, but death prevented the completion. In *Kosmos* Humboldt heaped further praise on Ritter's monumental work.

Though Ritter was primarily a human geographer and Humboldt a physical geographer, both worked throughout the range of the discipline; both men were masters of the total subject. But Humboldt was mainly interested in trying to establish laws to explain the physical environment, while Ritter emphasized man at the expense of the physical environment. He did not, however, ignore the physical setting. He established the physical framework and then placed man within it for study. In so doing Ritter pioneered in the creation of physical regions as a basis for regional human geography. Ritter used river basins, mountains, plateaus, hills, and plains to delineate these regions. *Erdkunde* includes such systematic cultural studies as plant and animal domestication, the historical geography of tea, the geographic distribution of cotton and its relationship to industry in antiquity and modern times, date palms, and even tigers.

Ritter has been criticized for permitting his religious beliefs to enter his work, which they certainly do. A deeply religious man, Ritter saw the earth as an organic whole, made to perfection. There was a divine arrangement of everything, and man's lot was pre-destined by God.

Ritter, the co-founder of modern geography, died in 1859, sharing even the year of his death with his good friend Humboldt.[2]

---

[2]The year 1859 marked the publication of Charles Darwin's *On the Origin of Species*, which was to alter the course of all science. Hettner, Boas, and Freud were born in 1859.

After 1859 the development of geographic thought was rapid. Essentially, this was a segment of the emerging scientific age that sprang from northwestern Europe. Germany, France, and Great Britain led the way, though there were major contributions from other countries that shared the north European tradition.

Though the progress of geography after the mid-nineteenth century may be traced in a variety of different ways, there appear to be four clear lines of evolution: (1) physical geography, (2) human geography, (3) regional geography, and (4) geographic techniques.

Physical Geography

Oscar Peschel (1826-1875) is usually credited with the establishment of modern physical geography in Germany. Building upon the work of Ritter, Peschel elaborated the comparative method. He attempted *explanation* rather than mere *classification* of earth features. His comparative study of the fjords of the world serves as a classic example of Peschel's work. Humboldt had made no attempt to classify landforms and Ritter had not bothered with explanation. With this in mind, then, Peschel's work sets a new course.[3]

But Peschel did not build his work on a vacuum. His proximity to Humboldt and Ritter is obvious, but there were earlier men to whom Peschel and physical geography owe much. As early as mid-eighteenth century, G. L. Leclerc de Buffon (1707-1788), the great French naturalist, was studying the earth's surface. Buffon's work, like that of most earth "scientists" up until the nineteenth century, held to the notion of the Universal Flood. Hence, his conclusions were forced to conform to that theory. Truly scientific earth science began with James Hutton (1726-1797) and John Playfair (1748-1819), both of Edinburgh, Scotland.

Hutton, in 1785, presented a paper titled *The Theory of the Earth*, in which he established the principle of *uniformitarianism*. This theory teaches that there was no beginning and no ending, and to Hutton it meant that all surface features result from the slow process of erosion caused by running water and atmospheric phenomena. In 1802, Playfair wrote a book (*Illustrations of the Huttonian Theory*) to explain his colleague's ideas.

The work of these two Scotsmen became the spark that led Charles Lyell to publish between 1830-1833 a three-volume work titled *The Prin-*

---

[3]Peschel's work of primary interest to geographers is *Neue Probleme der vergleichenden Erdkunde als Versuch einer Morphologie der Erdoberfläche* (1870). *Physische Erdkunde* (1879), a collection of papers published posthumously, is also significant.

ciples of Geology. Lyell's epic is credited with eliminating from modern science the theory of a catastrophic creation.

After Lyell's work appeared there was a rash of geomorphological studies, though not all resulted directly from Lyell's influence. Louis Agassiz (1807-1873), the famed Swiss naturalist (he came to Harvard in 1848), published the results of his work on glaciation in 1837, and suggested the concept of the Ice Age. In the United States, J. L. Lesley related topography to structure in his *Manual of Coal and Its Topography* (1856), but he did not treat landforms as evolutionary features. This idea was developed in the American west by such men as J. W. Powell (*Exploration of the Colorado River of the West,* 1875), G. K. Gilbert (*Geology of the Henry Mountains,* 1877), and C. E. Dutton (*Report on the Geology of the High Plateaus of Utah,* 1880).

The trend toward an evolutionary explanation of natural features that commenced in the nineteenth century had little to do with the biological evolution of Darwin. But it was a part of the same intellectual climate which, at least in part, arose as an opposition to the teleological notions of the previous 200 years.

In Europe physical geography (especially geomorphology) became increasingly important after Peschel. Ferdinand von Richthofen (1833-1905) began intensive geological work in the Tirol in 1856, and later extended this investigation to include Transylvania. In 1859 he journeyed to the Far East, visiting Ceylon, Japan, Taiwan, the Philippines, Java, Thailand, Burma, East Pakistan, and India. Unfortunately, his records were lost and little resulted from this extensive trip. He came to California for a stay of several years, but returned to Europe in 1868 and began a series of seven expeditions to China. The results of these travels were published in three volumes between 1877-1885 (*China: Ergebnisse eigner Reisen und darauf gegründeter Studien*).

Richthofen developed his theory of the aeolian origin of loess as a result of his China studies. He also devoted much of his attention to economic geology and made valuable contributions to human geography. In 1886 he published *Führer für Forschungsreisende,* in which he presents the first scientific classification of landforms.

Albrecht Penck (1856-1945) drew heavily on Richthofen's work for his own classification, which appeared in 1894 in a two-volume work titled *Morphologie der Erdoberfläche.* This work remains a standard reference in German.

In the United States, William Morris Davis (1850-1934) fathered geomorphology. His name is a household term among students of landforms, but few realize that his first contributions to physical geography were in the field of meteorology. Davis spent three years with the

Argentine Meteorological Observatory in Córdoba, and contributed 42 articles and one book (*Elementary Meteorology*, 1894) in that subject.

Davis' most important geomorphological contribution was the "cycle of erosion" or the "geographical cycle." Basically, the theory states that distinctive stages are recognizable as a region is reduced from its original form to the *peneplain* (Davis' own term for the last stage of erosion, or base level). The details of the theory are too well known to be repeated here, but it should be pointed out that Davis' critics have often misinterpreted the original words. Davis did permit interruption of his cycle (by tectonic or climatic change, for example), though his critics say he did not. Other charges against the Davisian system are: too little attention is given past climates, a developmental series of phenomena were established before the processes were known, deductive reasoning is not reliable, uplift was misinterpreted, "absolute age" is a questionable notion.

Nevertheless, Davis spurred people to study, to observe, and to react. Almost 300 publications in landforms came from his pen. He was one of the founders of the Association of American Geographers and became its first president in 1904. But the enthusiasm, at least in the United States, did not continue. After 1920, most geographers turned to some form of human study and the geologists turned to oil surveys. Geography continued to be studied in a physical regional setting (which may have created more problems than it solved), and the influence of Davis remains a major force in both physical and human geography.

Physical geography includes, in addition to studies concerning the lithosphere, those that deal with the hydrosphere, atmosphere, and biosphere. It is lamentable that geography has been willing to allow all four of these areas to drift from under its umbrella to a large degree. The separation was defended for many years because geography was supposed to be holding fast to its generalist and universal nature and was therefore not concerned with extreme forms of specialization. It is ironic that these highly specialized disciplines have swung full-circle and are now developing such interesting ideas as biometeorology and bioclimatology, geology and its relationship to man (the University of South Florida has a *geology* course titled *Hydrogeology and Human Affairs!*), and *human* oceanography.

Meteorology and climatology have always been a part of geography, but the former is almost lost to our discipline. Though there are roots into antiquity, and Edmund Halley (1656-1742) offered an explanation of the planetary wind system in the eighteenth century, the collection of records dates from the nineteenth century. Chevalier de Lamark (1774-1829) is credited with the latter (*Annuaires météorologiques*, 1800-1815) and after his time record-keeping provided the raw data for weather research. In the United States the Smithsonian Institution began daily reports in 1851; the British Meteorological Office was founded in 1854.

Climatology remained a moribund subject until the principles of meteorology were learned. Wladimir Köppen (1846-1940) pioneered modern climatology with a classification in 1884. His scheme reflects his training as a botanist. Best known is his classification of 1918, which was refined for publication in 1931 as *Grundriss der Klimakunde*. Later Köppen edited (with Rudolf Geiger) the five-volume *Handbuch der Klimatologie* (1930-1940), though the project was incomplete upon his death.

Alexander Supan gave us his classification (based on isotherms) in 1903, and the most recent significant classification system was derived by C. Warren Thornthwaite in 1931 (*The Climates of North America According to a New Classification*). His *The Climates of the Earth* appeared in 1933 and, since that time, a dedicated group of followers has attempted to improve Thornthwaite's basic plan and to gain general acceptance for it. A survey of standard textbooks in this country will, however, show that the modified Köppen system continues to be by far the most widely used climatic scheme employed by geographers.

During the last few years (especially since World War II) meteorology has developed its own profession and university departments. Climatology still remains within most major university organizations as part of geography, but a check of occupational preferences by members of the Association of American Geographers shows that climatology is a minor segment of today's geography.

The study of the hydrosphere (largely oceanography) never was as important to geography as studies relating to the land and air. For some reason geographers were willing at an early date to renounce 70 per cent of the earth's surface as a field of examination.

In 1855 there appeared a publication titled *The Physical Geography of the Sea*, by M. F. Maury (1806-1873), an American naval officer. Maury not only collected many years of ships' records, but he was able to map a portion of the North Atlantic ocean floor. Following Maury's early work there were several oceanographic expeditions. Between 1872-1877 the *Challenger* (English), *Tuscarora* (American), and *Gazelle* (German) surveyed much of the ocean surface. The *Challenger* voyage alone resulted in 50 published volumes of research findings.

Oceanography has developed almost independently of geography for over 100 years. Today not more than a handful of geographers contribute to oceanographic teaching or research. The field is dominated by physicists, chemists, marine geologists, and marine biologists, who seem to be unable to bring any order from their multitudinous investigations.

There appears to be room in oceanography for the well-trained generalist, and until that happens oceanography will be as incomprehensible as, say, something called "science." For one thing, oceanography needs a theory. Perhaps geography could make this contribution.

Biogeography is the fourth major physical branch of geography. The study of plants and animals, from geographic points of view, is an important (but regrettably small) part of our discipline. Humboldt showed the way in 1805 (*Essai sur la géographie des plantes*), but few followed his lead and botany and zoology claimed the field.

Today the works of A. W. Küchler and C. F. Bennett, in the areas of plant geography and animal geography, respectively, indicate the excitement and potential of the subject. The study of soil might also be included as part of the biosphere, at least as geographers approach the subject. There are even fewer soil geographers than biogeographers.

Without doubt, the study of physical geography is on the decline, but the study of the historic parts of physical geography is enjoying tremendous prestige (and financial support) *outside* the confines of geography. Further, geographers are not engaged in most of these studies beyond our limits. Is this because geography and geographers have nothing much to contribute any more to physical geography? Or is it because we have allied ourselves more to the social sciences and abandoned our traditional role as the bridge between natural and social science?

Human Geography

Modern human geography, like physical geography, is a product of nineteenth-century Europe, primarily Germany and France.

In Germany, Friedrich Ratzel (1844-1904) showed the way. Trained in geology and zoology, and later employed as a journalist, Ratzel turned to geography after touring the United States. (His impressions were published in 1878-1880 as *Die Vereinigten Staaten von Nordamerika*). After several positions Ratzel followed Richthofen as professor of geography at Leipzig, in 1883.

Just before he accepted this chair he published the first volume of *Anthropogeographie* (1882), The second volume appeared in 1891, while his *magnum opus, Völkerkunde* (translated as *The History of Mankind*) fell in between.

The first volume of *Anthropogeographie* emphasized the point that man is a product of his physical environment. Though acknowledging the fact that nature is not the only thing which determines the course of human action, Ratzel quite clearly set the stage for a more rigid formulation of his thesis. Later, in the second volume, Ratzel stresses the influence of man on nature, but the damage had been done, and students, like Ellen Churchill Semple (1863-1932), carried Ratzel's ideas (often modified) to America. Her interpretation of Ratzel in *American History and its Geographic Conditions* (1903) and in *Influences of Geographic Environment on the Basis of Ratzel's System of Anthropogeography* (1911) transmuted Ratzel's rather acceptable position (especially after volume II appeared) into one which held that the environment of *all* peoples is the determining factor in shaping their cultures. Miss Semple's influence, from positions held at the University of Chicago and Clark University, was a major factor underlying the direction of American geography between the two World Wars.

Ratzel unwittingly gave the world modern environmental determinism. And his notion of an organic state, so carefully detailed in his last work, *Politische Geographie* (1897) furnished much grist for the mill of the German *Geopolitik* that was to emerge during the Nazi era. The organic-state concept is not new to German philosophy (Kant, Hegel, and Nietzsche, for example, espoused it), and it is a further instance of how the ideas of a great pioneer geographer were twisted. Ratzel's work is too profound to be censored by academic opinion, and a full translation of *Anthropogeographie* is long overdue. It was Ratzel, after all, that made human geography a science.

To follow the thread, let us mention Ellsworth Huntington (1876-1947) of Yale University and Griffith Taylor (1880-1963), long at the University of Toronto. These men followed the environmentalist path into the 1940's. Both wrote prolifically; both were exceptionally fine lecturers. Their influence was of marked import for years, and Huntington's books still remain bestsellers, even appearing in paperback editions on newsstands.

Geographers became so reluctant to deal with the natural environment and man after the environmentalists were essentially discredited that this may partially explain the waning of physical geography in the United States. Geographers today would hardly publish a journal of biometeorology or bioclimatology (as the meteorologists do) for fear of being branded geographic determinists. It is surely time that we in the discipline overcame this timidity and began to re-think the whole problem of man and nature.

Human geography in Europe never went through the period of environmentalism to the degree that it did in North America. For one thing the German followers of Ratzel stressed regional rather than man-land geography. For another, an important school developed in France that offered an alternative to extreme viewpoints.

In Germany, Alfred Hettner (1859-1941), a student of Richthofen, saw geography as the areal differentiation of the earth's surface. Though he based his work on physical aspects and saw no way to separate man from the earth, he held the region to be central. Hettner gave geography its first major work on methodology (*Das Wesen und die Methoden der Geographie*, 1905) and this, along with his important position at Heidelberg from 1898-1935, made him one to be listened to.[4]

In France there was an instant and violently negative reaction to Ratzel's work, though France was not without its own small group of environmentalists. This group was largely composed of followers of Frederic Leplay (1806-1882). Like Ratzel's adherents in America, Leplay's students corrupted the teachings of their master. Leplay built a new method for sociology by insisting that the primary occupations be considered (farming, hunting, fishing, herding, etc.) and by stating that the environment must be related to the occupation of the population, and that the occupation is related to the social organization of the people. Leplay's successors claimed that social organization rested on the environment.

Though many reacted to the determinism of Ratzel and of Leplay's group (such as the sociologist Durkheim and anthropologist Marett), for geography the opposition was led by Paul Vidal de la Blache (1845-1918), and his brilliant student Jean Brunhes (1869-1930).

Vidal was a student of the works of Humboldt and Ritter. He was a professor of geography at the École Normale Supérieure from 1877-1898, and went to the Sorbonne in 1898 to remain until his death. He published many articles and several books that illustrate his general philosophy. Basically, Vidal was a regional geographer who believed that cause and effect must be studied. Further, he held that nature offered man a number of possibilities, and that man made the choice. Tradition, he believed, might cause some people to overlook alternative ways of behavior, Lucien Febvre, in 1925, labeled this concept *possibilism.*

Vidal's students produced a vast quantity of detailed synthetic studies, mostly concerning the regions of France. His foremost student in human geography was Jean Brunhes who, in 1907, was appointed to the first chair of human geography in Europe. This was at Lausanne, Switzerland, though he left to accept a similar chair at the Collège de France (Paris) in 1912. Brunhes' book *Human Geography* (in an English translation) would be used today if it were in print. Brunhes also published significant works on irrigation and *Geography of History* (1921).

Brunhes departed from the strict regionalism of his teacher. This was due largely to the fact that he wanted the freedom to study culture elements across regional lines. To Brunhes human geography was never static and he believed that the role of the physical environment had been

---

[4]Hettner's other major work of interest to students of geographical development is *Die Geographiesihre Geschichte, ihr Wesen, und ihre Methoden,* 1927.

exaggerated by geographers. To prove this he suggested that the distribution of house types in France was determined by historic causes and not by climate or landforms.

Brunhes and Hettner (who also was interested in the study of culture elements) had a great influence on American *cultural* geographers.

Today human geography is becoming sharply divided between social and cultural geography. The former is urban and population oriented; the latter, rural and area (space) oriented. Cultural geography is deeply rooted in history, anthropology, and is closely related to rural sociology; social geography is concerned with the industrial-manufacturing-transportation-urban-population syndrome and is tied closely with sociology, urban anthropology, and economics. Social geography is inextricably bound to statistics and census material, while cultural geographers more often than not rely on their own field-collected data. The rural (cultural)-urban (social) dichotomy in modern human geography is a serious rift, with a much greater gap between many of the followers of each school than between physical and cultural geography. In the latter instance, cultural geographers, following the German development, place great emphasis on the physical landscape as the stage upon which culture operates. Social geographers (especially the more quantitatively oriented ones) have a tendency to ignore the physical setting. Once the connection is dropped between man and land there is some question as to whether it is still geography and/or whether or not someone trained in another discipline might not be able to do the job just as well.

Regional Geography

There are too many works extant in English (and in American journals) to linger on the development of regional geography (see especially *The Nature of Geography,* by Richard Hartshorne, AAG, 1939). But its significance does require us to pause for a moment of consideration.

Modern regionalism comes to us from France and Germany, and most modern geographers are regionalists, whether they admit it or not. Even the devout systematic geographers usually organize their studies in a regional manner, and the region is the one thing geographers can proudly claim as their own, even though some may shudder at the very thought.

For many culture-element geographers, the idea that they are bound hand and foot with regional geography is difficult to believe. Yet it is quite the case.

The study of culture-elements in the United States has come from August Meitzen (1882-1910), Otto Schlüter (1872-1959), Alfred Hettner, and Jean Bruhnes. In the main, their ideas came into this country first through the writings of Carl Sauer, and secondly through the work of Sauer's students at the University of California (and their students). Of the German school, Schlüter has had the most direct influence.

The first important American statement on geographic methodology came in 1925 from Sauer (in *The Morphology of Landscape*). He said, in essence, that the goal of geography is a world pattern of regions, of greater or lesser magnitude, which can be placed in generic relationship to each other. Sauer departed from Hettner by arguing that the landscape is an association of visible cultural and physical things (Hettner would have included invisible features). He borrowed his term "morphology" from Ritter, and saw the morphologic method as a way to approach structure from the functions of its parts.

This paper brought American regional geography into its own. And Sauer's students covered the Americas with regional studies. Though many of the California School are element-oriented, the final product is often highly regionalist. Even so, it was one of Sauer's students (John Leighly) who attacked regional geography so vigorously (in *Some Comments on Contemporary Geographic Method*, 1937) that it in part prompted Hartshorne to respond with his classic *The Nature of Geography*, which is a masterful defense of regionalism.

For 30 years there has raged a pitched battle (usually conducted on polite terms) between the regionalists and the anti-regionalists. A check of any university catalog will give some indication as to how the struggle goes and which side is represented at the given institution.

Geographic Techniques

Cartography was, is, and shall continue to remain the fundamental geographic tool. Like all techniques, it is a means to an end, never the end in itself. Much of this study has dealt with the development of cartography, for without it there would be no geography. Today cartographic techniques have become highly sophisticated. Computers can produce a read-out that with a modicum of touch-up becomes a map (many weather maps are computer-plotted). To one tool we have appended another, the computer.

Rapid data analysis (and synthesis) can be accomplished by means of computers. There is nothing new in the collection of statistics; only the tools have evolved. Quantitative methods, seen by some as a threat and by others as a passing fancy, are really an elaboration of old techniques. Unfortunately, for some quantitative geographers the means has become an end, and they might find a warmer welcome in some circles if they would reevaluate the relationship between tool and product.

Photography has gained in importance as a geographic technique. Aerial photography has long been a basic adjunct of research. This has been refined to include remote sensing of the environment from aircraft and spacecraft (especially by means of infra-red techniques) and television coverage on video tape that can be examined inch-by-inch in the laboratory.

The greatest danger inherent in the new techniques is that their sheer complexity of mathematics and electronics can cause a blurring of the ultimate goals of geography. Other disciplines use the same tools, and some tool-users (say, in engineering) might well handle them far more efficiently. If geography is not careful in the next few, critical years it may find that more and more aspects of it will be absorbed by other disciplines. As long as we remain a science of *place* there is nothing to fear. If the arms and legs begin to control the head the consequences may well be unpleasant.

Chapter 10

Diffusion from the Hearth

Geography becomes Universal

After the establishment of modern geography in Germany there was a brief period of indecision. Ritter's first chair in geography at Berlin was unoccupied for some years after his death, and the first English chair of geography (held in the 1830's by Alexander Maconochie) went unfilled after he resigned.[1] Though France had a long tradition in geography, as evidenced by attempts to form a geographical society as early as 1785 (the Société de Géographie de Paris, 1821, is the world's first such organization), the real drive does not seem to have begun until the Franco-Prussian War and Vidal de la Blache.

We have already mentioned certain non-continental developments (mainly in Great Britain and the United States) that occurred as a direct off-shoot of nineteenth-century European geography. It is now time to briefly note developments around the world, for geography, especially since World War II, has found a home in many new nations.

The summary that follows is selective, and the countries chosen are represented by at least one major geographical society. It is largely from an examination of the journals of these societies that trends and developments have been determined.[2]

Europe

Germany (East and West)

Although German geography has been traditionally strong in physical and regional studies, culture-element and economic geography are becoming increasingly important. With the possible exception of France,

---

[1]Broek, p. 16.
[2]Harris, *Annotated Lists.* . . .

Germany possesses a unification of geographic purpose unknown in the rest of the world. Physical and human geography occupy well-defined positions; the latter is always based soundly on the former.

Journals

Erde (1853-   ), Berlin Geographical Society
Erdkunde (1947-   ), Geographic Institute of the University of Bonn
Geographische Berichte (1956-   ), Geographical Society of the German Democratic Republic
Geographische Rundschau (1949-   ), commercial publication
Geographische Zeitschrift (1895-1944; 1963-   ), Geographic Institute of the University of Heidelberg
Geographisches Taschenbuch (1949-   ), Institute for Geography, Michaelshof, Bad Godesberg
Petermanns Geographische Mitteilungen (1855-   ), Geographical Society of the German Democratic Republic

France

French geography has long suffered from disunity. This is due, in large measure, to the organization of the French university system, where there is a rigid division between the Faculty of Sciences and the Faculty of Letters. It is in the latter, in connection with history, where advanced geography is taught. Though this arrangement has produced a highly sophisticated series of historical geographic studies, it has also led to second-class status for geography, which is often considered a step-child of history. Physical geography occupies a world of its own, often on the other side of town. This is quite unlike Germany, where both human and physical geography are within the Faculty of Philosophy. This system encourages the placement of human studies on a physical base; French cultural geographers often have no training whatsoever in the natural sciences. Vidal de la Blache tried to overcome this, by urging his students to take work in the Faculty of Sciences *after* completing their work in Letters.

This confusion is readily discerned in the journals, which have had an erratic history in France. Today, only the *Annales de Géographie,* which began publishing in 1891 (with Jean Brunhes as one of the first directors), displays any continuity. And it is a commercial publication.

The *Société de Géographie de Paris* published the *Bulletin* from 1822-1899. Between 1900-1939 it was known as *La Géographie*. After World War II (in 1947) the Society began publishing the *Acta Geographica*.

The *Annales* has long been oriented toward physical geography, and human geography has declined. There are a number of French journals dedicated to specialized fields (alpine studies, geomorphology, etc.) that are of interest to geographers.

United Kingdom

One might judge from the clamor in this country that all British geography is quantitative, but that is not generally the case. Most of the quantitative influence in the U.S. has come from the University of Bristol. Judging by the journals, the British School of Quantification has more members overseas than at home.

Geography in the United Kingdom remains strongly regional, with physical and economic segments occupying important places. Since 1925 historical geography has been on the rise. H. C. Darby's *Domesday* studies (at the University of London) were primarily responsible for this interest. The University College of Wales (Aberystwyth), whose department of Geography was founded by H. J. Fleure, has been a leading center for cultural studies.

Generally the British have not been concerned much with methodology and theory. Some of Fleure's pre-historical geography might not even be geography; it leans so heavily toward anthropology that British geographers have often asked the famous question, "Is that geography?" The same question has been put to the quantifiers recently. Maybe these two extremes will prompt the British to make a serious inquiry into the nature of geography. Perhaps it has been a prime force in driving the quantifiers to seek a theory of their own.

Journals

Geographical Journal (1830-   ), Royal Geographical Society
Publications of the Institute of British Geographers (1935-   ), Department of Geography, Cambridge University
East Midland Geographer (1954-   ), Department of Geography, Nottingham University
Geography (1901-   ), Geographical Association
Geographical Abstracts (1960-   ), Department of Geography, London School of Economics
Scottish Geographical Magazine (1885-   ), Royal Scottish Geographical Society
Geographical Magazine (1935-   ), commercial publication
New Geographical Literature and Maps (1951-   ), Royal Geographical Society

Scandinavia

Scandinavia inherited much of its geographic tradition from Germany, and especially from Hettner. Helge Nelson, who has worked mainly with Swedish settlements in the United States and Canada, is credited with bringing Hettner's ideas to Sweden.

The balance between physical and human geography is rather well maintained but regional geography has been on the decline. In Sweden, regional geography enjoyed some popularity 35-40 years ago, but today it has almost disappeared from the journals. The demise of regional work in Sweden is more complete than in any other western country.

Physical geography in Scandinavia has long been important, especially in the areas of meteorology, climatology, glaciology, and geomorphology. The Geographical Institute of the University of Copenhagen is a principal center for physical studies.

Human geography is just as well developed as physical, and several centers are noted for work in this branch. At Aarhus, Denmark, the Geographical Institute of the University is oriented toward human geography, and has done pioneering work on the origin of irrigation and settlement geography.

Denmark's two leading journals, like its two major geographical centers, indicate the equal division of physical and cultural geography. The *Geografisk Tidsskrift* (Royal Danish Geographical Society) has been published since 1877. It is a distinguished journal that contains many systematic physical studies. *Kulturgeografi* began in 1949 at Aarhus. It publishes articles on cultural, social, economic, and political geography.

Sweden's main organs are summarized. *Geografiska Annaler* (Swedish Anthropological and Geographical Society), established in 1919; publishes three issues out of four in physical geography. The *Lund Studies in Geography* (Lund University) appear in three series. *Series A* (1950-), physical geography; *Series B* (1949-), human geography; *Series C* (1962-), general and mathematical geography (especially quantitative and photo interpretation). The *Svensk Geografisk Årsbok* (Geographical Society of Southern Sweden) dates from 1925 and publishes general articles. *Ymer* (Swedish Anthropological and Geographical Society) began in 1881. It is primarily a popular publication with a heavy economic bent.

Fennia (Finnish Geographical Society) dates from 1889, and publishes a wide range of articles, but stresses Finland and Scandinavia. *Terra* is of the same age and origin, and deals with general geography and Finland.

Norway's principal journal, *Norsk Geografisk Tidsskrift* (Norwegian Geographical Society), was established in 1926 and is heavy on glacial and geomorphological studies.

Before departing Scandinavia, mention should be made of three men. Adolph E. Nordenskiöld was the father of Swedish geography and served as the first president of the Anthropological and Geographical Society (which grew out of a purely anthropological organization founded in 1873). Nordenskiöld was a geologist, arctic explorer, and historian of geography and geographic discovery. Erland Nordenskiöld (son of

Adolph) became an anthropologist with a geographer's approach. His comparative ethnography in South America is well known. Lastly Stan De Geer (who died in 1933) was a leading cartographer (he gave geography those little globes used on maps to represent volume, and he was the first to use dot maps for population distribution). De Geer wrote on methodology (*What Geography Is*, 1925), and he is one of the founders of the urban/economic movement in modern geography.

Switzerland

Like Scandinavia, Switzerland places equal emphasis on human and physical geography. *Le Globe,* published by the Geographical Society of Geneva since 1860, is one of Europe's oldest journals. It is essentially an outlet for physical geography. *Geographica Helvetica* is a post-war journal (1946-   ), but had a forerunner (the *Mitteilungen*), also sponsored by the Geographical-Ethnological Society of Zurich. This is a human-oriented bulletin, though geomorphological articles form an important part of the whole. Cartography has also received more attention since 1946.

Italy

Italian geography is organized in such a way that each university is a specialist in one particular phase of the subject. The five leading institutions are: Bologna (physical), Florence (ethno-geographical), Rome (human), Naples (economic), and the Museum of Natural History (alpine studies).

Four important journals grace Italian scholarship. The *Annali di Ricerche e Studi di Geografia* (1945-   ) is published by the Institute of Geography, University of Genoa. The Italian Geographical Society publishes the *Bollettino* (1868-   ). The Society of Geographic Studies produces the *Rivista Geogràfica Italiana* (1893-   ), which is the country's leading journal. *Universo* is an organ of the Military Geographic Institute (1920-   ).

Spain and Portugal

A very few words can sum up Spanish geography before 1939: it was pretty poor. Generally encyclopaedic in nature, Spain's main contribution was in the re-publication of sixteenth-century *relaciones geográficas*. Many of these appeared in the *Boletín* of the Royal Geographical Society (Geographical Society of Madrid between 1876-1901). The *Boletín* is still published and strives to maintain its miserable record.

After the civil war the *Consejo Superior de Investigaciones Cientí-ficas* was formed (1939). Various institutes were established under the jurisdiction of the *Consejo*. The *Instituto "Juan Sebastián Elcano"* was established in Madrid, with branches in Barcelona and Zaragoza. *Estudios Geográficos* began publication in 1940. *Pirineos* is the journal of the Institute for Pyrenees Studies: *Revista Antropología y Etnología* is the outlet for the institute of the same name; *Speleón* deals with hydrology, karst morphology, and speliology.

There are several important Spanish geographers today and the field is beginning to develop. Physical studies head the last of subjects, per-haps because the father of modern Spanish geography, Juan Dantín Cereceda, was a geomorphologist. However, he was also interested in human geography.

The Geographical Society of Lisbon has published the *Boletim* since 1876. It sticks pretty closely to articles dealing with Portugal, its overseas interests, Brazil, and early exploration.

East Europe and the U.S.S.R.

Each of the East European states has at least one national geographic journal. They are largely dominated by (1) national studies, (2) physical geography, and (3) economic geography. A few of the journals represent long traditions. The *Geographical Review* of Hungary (*Földrajzi Köz-lemények*) dates from 1873; the *Journal* (*Sborník*) of the Czechoslovak Geographical Society goes back to 1894.

The USSR has several important publications. The main university organ is *Geografiia*, published by Moscow University since 1960. *Geo-graficheskaia* (1951-   ) is a product of the Russian Academy of Sciences and is the USSR's most comprehensive journal. *Geograficheskoe Obshchestvo SSSR* (1865-   ) is the country's oldest journal and stresses physical geography.

The development of Soviet Geography has followed the needs of the state. Especially important are physical, soils, climate, vegetation, and economic research into raw materials and their handling. For a detailed understanding of Soviet geography, see *Soviet Geography: Review and Translation* (American Geographical Society), and for the development of geographic thought in the USSR see David Hooson's article "The Development of Geography in Pre-Soviet Russia" (cited in Bibliog-raphy). Hooson traces Russian geography from the seventeenth century to the present. His discussion points out that Russian geography, though eventually developing a strong national character, was strongly influ-enced by Western thought (particularly German) during most of this time. The most distinctive features of modern Soviet geography are investigations into heat and water balance, the concept of *natural zones,* and regional studies (especially the construction of synthetic economic regions).

Afro-Asia

Many of the newly emerging states have established university programs and government institutes of geography. Only the United Arab Republic has a journal of long-standing (the *Bulletin* of the *Société de Géographie d'Égypte,* founded in 1876). A few nations had journals by the 1920's, but most of them are post-World War II, and many are as new as the 1960's. Typically the new states pattern their approaches to geography after the mother countries, for most of their professional geographers received their training there.

Japan's interest is presently divided among physical, human, and economic geography, and there is a society and journal reflecting each point of view. Japanese geography is organized very much like that in the United States, both in professional societies and in universities.

Latin America

Mexico has the oldest geographical serial in the Americas, the *Boletín* of the *Sociedad Mexicana de Geografía y Estadística* (founded 1839). The *Anuario de Geografía* (National University of Mexico) is a new publication (1961) but it is an excellent one, containing articles mainly on Mexico.

Argentina, Brazil, Chile, Colombia, Costa Rica, Cuba, Peru, and Venezuela all have major publications. Most of these deal with the geography of the country involved, and the many regional publications of Argentina and Brazil treat specifically of those local areas. Physical geography is strongly represented in Latin America, and there is an interest in historical geography (especially of the colonial period).

The English-Speaking Rimland

Canada, Australia, New Zealand, South Africa, and several former colonial states (such as India) represent traditions derived directly from Europe but modified locally. Generally, each of the ex-European states has an active group of geographers. A large variety of publications flow from these areas and all reflect, to some extent, the geography of the states themselves. New Zealand geographers, for example, devote considerable attention to the Pacific; Canadians have long investigated the arctic and subarctic.

Geography in these countries is closely aligned to that in the United States and the United Kingdom. Teachers move with ease among countries with a common language and culture, and it appears that a universal geographic approach is emerging that is barely distinguishable from place to place (except as local regional specialization varies).

Perhaps the United States should be placed with this group. An analysis of any of the publications listed (below) will indicate the similarity of interests and the evident cross-fertilization.

Annals of the Association of American Geographers (1911-   )
Economic Geography (1925-   ), Clark University, U. S.
Geographical Review (1852-   ), American Geographical Society
Journal of Geography (1902-   ), National Council for Geographic Education, U.S.
Professional Geographer (1949-   ), AAG
Australian Geographer (1928-   ), Geographical Society of New South Wales
Canadian Geographer (1951-   ), Canadian Association of Geographers
Geographical Review of India (1936-   ), Geographical Society of India
Indian Geographical Journal (1926-   ), Indian Geographical Society
New Zealand Geographer (1945-   ), New Zealand Geographical Society
South African Geographical Journal (1917-   ), South African Geographical Society

Of course, the above list is highly selective and the reader is referred to the bibliography (see Harris) for additional items. But the expansion of journal literature to cover all aspects of our discipline, and all parts of our planet, is an effective summary to our story.

Geography has been traced from the time a pre-literate man of 10,000 years ago wondered about the things around him to an age when it is humanly impossible to absorb all the material written about those same surroundings. When the story of geography began man could stand on a hill and view his entire world; by Christmastime of 1968 three American astronauts (Borman, Lovell, and Anders, in *Apollo 8*) were able to view their world from the vantage point of a lunar orbit. It is fitting that we end this brief study with mention of the greatest voyage ever undertaken by man.

The future may well see geographers in space. To prepare for the things to come we must preserve a tradition broad enough to encompass lunar and planetary investigations, much as the ancient Greeks laid the foundation for a discipline that now finds itself 2000 years from the Aegean. In (and beyond) a world becoming increasingly specialized, perhaps geography is the one science left that specializes in generalization. If not geographers who, then, will pull all of the pieces together?

Appendix

Geographical Specialties Claimed by American Geographers in 1968

Administration
Agricultural Geography
Air Photo Interpretation
Anthropogeography
Applied Geography
Arid Regions Geography
Audio-Visual Materials
Biogeography
Cartography, General
Cartography, Theoretical
Cartography, Thematic
Climatology
Coastal Geography
Conservation
Cultural Geography
Economic Geography
Educational Geography
Electronic Data Processing
Environmental Geography
Field Methods
Geographic Techniques
Geology
Geomorphology
Historical Geography
History of Geography
Industrial Geography
Interdisciplinary Activities
Land Use
Librarianship, Geographical

Manufacturing Geography
Marketing Geography
Medical Geography
Meteorology
Military Geography
Mountain Geography
Oceanography
Philosophy of Geography
Photogrammetry
Physical Geography
Planning, Regional
Planning, Urban
Plant Geography
Political Geography
Population Geography
Quantitative Methods
Recreational Geography
Regional Geography
Remote Sensing
Resource Geography
Rural Geography
Soils Geography
Teaching Techniques
Toponomy
Transportation & Communication
Tropical Geography
Urban Geography
Water Resources
Zoogeography

Selected Bibliography

AHARONI, Y., and AVI-YONAH, M. *The Macmillan Bible Atlas*, New York: The Macmillan Co., 1968.

BARROWS, H. H. "Geography as Human Ecology," *Annals of the AAG*, XIII (1923), 1-14.

BROEK, J. O. M. *Geography: Its Scope and Spirit*, Columbus: Charles E. Merrill Books, Inc., 1965.

BRUHNES, J. *Human Geography* (Abridged ed., Trans. by E. F. Row), Chicago: Rand McNally & Company, 1952.

BUNBURY, E. H. *A History of Ancient Geography* (2 vols.), New York: Dover Publications, Inc., 1959.

BUTLER, S. (Trans.) *The Iliad of Homer and The Odyssey*, Chicago: Encyclopaedia Britannica, Inc., 1952.

CAMERON, I. *Lodestone and Evening Star: The Epic Voyages of Discovery 1493 B.C.–1896 A.D.*, New York: E. P. Dutton & Co., Inc., 1966.

CANBY, C. (Ed.) *The Epic of Man*, New York: Time Incorporated, 1961.

CHORLEY, R. J. and HAGGETT, P. (Eds.) *Frontiers in Geographical Teaching*, London: Methuen & Co., Ltd., 1967.

CRONE, G. R. *Modern Geographers*, London: Royal Geographical Society, 1951.

———, *Royal Geographic Society: A Record. 1931-1955*, London, RGS, 1956.

DAVIS, W. M. *Geographical Essays*, New York: Dover Publications, Inc., 1954.

DE MARTONNE, E. *Geography in France*, New York: American Geographical Society, 1924.

DICKINSON, R. E. and HOWARTH, O. J. R. *The Making of Geography*, Oxford: Clarendon Press, 1933.

Encyclopaedia Britannica (23 vols.), Chicago: Encyclopaedia Britannica, Inc., 1965.

FENNEMAN, N. "The Circumference of Geography," *Annals of the AAG*, IX (1919), 3-11.

FREEMAN, T. W. *A Hundred Years of Geography*, Chicago: Aldine Publishing Co., 1962.

HARRIS, C. D. *Annotated List of Selected Current Geographical Serials of the Americas and the Iberian Peninsula*, Chicago: University of Chicago, 1967.

———, *Annotated World List of Selected Current Geographical Serials in English* (2nd ed.), Chicago: University of Chicago, 1964.

HARTSHORNE, R. *The Nature of Geography* (Vol. XXIX, Nos. 3-4, *Annals of the Association of American Geographers*), Lancaster: Association of American Geographers, 1939.

———, *Perspective on the Nature of Geography*, Chicago: Rand McNally & Co., 1959.

HETTNER, A. "Das Wesen und die Methoden der Geographie," *Geographische Zeitschrift*, XI (1905), 545-564; 615-629; 671-686.

————, *Die Geographie*: *ihre Geschichte, ihr Wesen, und ihre Methoden,* Breslau: F. Hirt, 1927.

HOOSON, D. J. M. "The Development of Geography in Pre-Soviet Russia," *Annals of the AAG,* LVIII (1968), 250-272.

JAMES, P. E. and JONES, C. F. *American Geography: Inventory and Prospect,* Syracuse: Syracuse University Press, 1954.

JONES, H. L. (Trans.) *The Geography of Strabo,* London: Wm. Heinemann, Ltd., 1917.

JOWELL, B. (Trans.) *The Dialogues of Plato,* Chicago: Encyclopaedia Britannica, Inc., 1952.

KELTIE, J. S. *The Position of Geography in the British Universities,* New York: American Geographical Society, 1921.

LEIGHLY, J. "Some Comments on Contemporary Geographic Method," *Annals of the AAG,* XXVII (1937), 125-141.

LEY, C. D. (Ed.) *Portuguese Voyages: 1498-1663,* London: J. M. Dent & Sons, Ltd., 1947.

MILL, H. R. *The Record of the Royal Geographic Society, 1830-1930,* London: RGS, 1930.

POHL, F. J. *Atlantic Crossings Before Columbus,* New York: W. W. Norton & Co., Inc., 1961.

RAISZ, E. *General Cartography,* New York: McGraw-Hill Book Co., 1948.

RAWLINSON, G. (Trans.) *The History of Herodotus,* Chicago: Encyclopaedia Britannica, Inc., 1952.

ROSS, W. D. (Trans.) *The Works of Aristotle,* Chicago: Encyclopaedia Britannica, Inc., 1952.

SAUER, C. O. "The Morphology of Landscape," *University of California Publications in Geography,* II (1925), 19-53.

SEMPLE, E. C. *Influences of Geographic Environment,* New York: Henry Holt & Co., 1911.

SINGER, C., et al (Eds.) *A History of Technology* (5 vols), London: Oxford University Press, 1954-1958.

Soviet Geography: Review & Translation, New York: American Geographical Society, 1960-1968.

TAYLOR, G. (Ed.) *Geography in the Twentieth Century,* New York: Philosophical Library, 1957.

The Bible (King James Version).

The Status of Geography in Countries Adhering to the I.G.U., (XVIIth IGC), Washington: International Geographical Union, 1952.

WOOLDRIDGE, S. W. and EAST, W. G. *The Spirit and Purpose of Geography,* London: Hutchinson University Library, 1951.

WRIGHT, J. K. *Geography in the Making,* New York: American Geographical Society, 1952.

Index